THE WEALTH FROM HEALTH PLAYBOOK

The Dramatic Path Forward in Healthcare Spawned by the Covid-19 Pandemic

Douglas Ratner, MD
Susan Walsh, MD, FACP

Universal-Publishers
Irvine • Boca Raton

The Wealth from Health Playbook:
The Dramatic Path Forward in Healthcare Spawned by the Covid-19 Pandemic

Universal Publishers, Inc.
Irvine • Boca Raton
USA • 2021
www.Universal-Publishers.com

ISBN: 978-1-62734-331-2 (pbk.)
ISBN: 978-1-62734-332-9 (ebk.)

Typeset by Medlar Publishing Solutions Pvt Ltd, India
Cover design by Ivan Popov

Library of Congress Cataloging-in-Publication Data

Names: Ratner, Douglas, 1952- author. | Walsh, Susan, author.
Title: The wealth from health playbook : the dramatic path forward in healthcare
    spawned by the COVID-19 pandemic / Douglas Ratner, MD, Susan Walsh, MD,
    FACP.
Description: Irvine : Universal Publishers, [2021] | Includes bibliographical references.
Identifiers: LCCN 2021000008 (print) | LCCN 2021000009 (ebook) |
    ISBN 9781627343312 (paperback) | ISBN 9781627343329 (ebook)
Subjects: LCSH: Telecommunication in medicine. | Telecommunication in
    medicine--United States. | Medical care--Technological innovations. |
    COVID-19 (Disease)
Classification: LCC R119.9 .R38 2021 (print) | LCC R119.9 (ebook) |
    DDC 610.285--dc23
LC record available at https://lccn.loc.gov/2021000008
LC ebook record available at https://lccn.loc.gov/2021000009

"To understand the actual world as it is, not as we should wish it to be, is the beginning of wisdom."
—Bertrand Russell

CONTENTS

EPILOGUE

APPENDIX ONE

APPENDIX TWO
Jersey City Medical Center-RWJ Barnabas Health System's
Quality Improvement Projects Initiative—an Abbreviated

APPENDIX THREE

ACKNOWLEDGMENTS

Five years ago, our CEO of RWJ Barnabas Health-Jersey City Medical Center, a large urban hospital in the most densely populated county in New Jersey, advised me that the former Deputy Commissioner of Health, Susan Walsh, MD, was available to hire for our fledgling Population Health Initiative. He spoke quite highly of her so, naturally, I called her and we agreed to meet to discuss a possible position to head up our effort in this initiative. She remembers, I think fondly, of the meeting, in which I apparently described her later to colleagues as "collegial," though I rarely use that word in my day-to-day conversations, as it is a little formal for my taste. Anyway, her biggest concern was whether there would be enough on her table to keep her busy. I assured her that would not be an issue and, after reading this book, I will let you answer that yourself.

To say that working together with Sue has been the highlight of my career would not be doing it justice. Though some people might think me a "visionary" or "delusional", Sue never wavered in her support and, more importantly, in her uncanny and highly professional ability to implement any solid idea into a *fait accompli*. Sue's adroitness continued to display itself by her assembly of the Wealth from Health team, whose marvelous work matched their wealth of kindness and empathy for the patients in our various initiatives.

Special thanks to Kwaku Gyekye, whose abilities and quiet fortitude kept our group humming and functioning at the highest of levels at all times and whose knowledge of the federal bundled payments (BPCI, Medicare) and Delivery System Reform Incentive Payment (DSRIP, Medicaid) programs kept those projects always hitting their marks. To Louis Alerte, who I admired the moment he entered the office for his interview for his statistical knowledge at the outset, but later for his limitless creativity and teaching ability. Louis almost singlehandedly assembled our Healthcare Leadership and Innovation curriculum that became a runaway success. Both men have an extremely bright future in healthcare administration.

Below is a list of our Wealth for Health team, which for the longest time was directed and supervised by one of the most capable nurses I have ever had the privilege to know, Ms. Jennifer Morales-Carvajal. Only later to be succeeded beautifully by Ms. Sharnia Williams.

Jobs well done, everyone, to which the national Hearst Healthcare Innovation Award (finalist), and Gage Award (Innovation Winner for America's Essential Hospitals), and state-based N.J. Population Health Hero Award all attest.

Douglas Ratner, MD

Wealth from Health team 2014–2017:
Kenny King
Audrey Williams
Jestina Kebbe
Yvonne Selloroli, RN
Judy Hoang
Garrick Hall
Raushanah Ali
Candice Pimental
Kim Dawson

INTRODUCTION

The name **Wealth from Health (WfH),** simply addresses a reality I observed both early in my medical career as a physician and personally. No matter who you are, without good health, all the money in the world pales in comparison, and that is the paradox. Suffice it to say that the older one gets, the more one becomes acutely aware of this fact. All our efforts through the Wealth from Health initiatives aim to emphasize this point repeatedly; to illustrate it, we reward all efforts at self-management with credits that are redeemable by rewards. These rewards are dwarfed, however, by the true "wealth" we all desire: good health. There are those who think that healthcare delivery is the same for all Americans, when it's obvious that is false. Perhaps they choose to believe such an absurdity because it satisfies their political talking points or assuages their guilt. But that still doesn't make it true, especially when a global pandemic debilitates the U.S. healthcare system and is responsible for an overwhelming number of deaths.

There remains no question that the COVID-19 pandemic of 2020 will provide the monumental shakeup and future road map for the healthcare industry. How can it not? The pandemic has threatened to last until a vaccine is developed and possibly beyond, while other viruses are certain to emerge as well, tragically. But the American people boast a long history of turning what appears to be a catastrophic occurrence into something positive. Necessity does indeed become the mother of invention.

The simple truth is that our healthcare system was severely dysfunctional years before COVID-19 reared its deadly presence and required a major overhaul. The discussion among the politicians continues to revolve around who pays for it and its affordability, certainly important issues. However, understanding how the system is woefully out of step with the wants and needs of the American people is crucial to getting its new infrastructure correctly configured.

During the "Great Pause" as this period has been labeled, I began to perform telemedicine consults through the Teladoc network and experienced an eureka moment, an epiphany, if you will. In a medium that I have been advocating for two decades, I have already performed hundreds of video and telephone consults for conditions commonly seen in an office setting (approximately 25% have been COVID-19 related). My studied observations are as follows:

1. Using telemedicine is a game changer because it is so easy for both the patient and the provider. (The Cleveland Clinic, for example, in Ohio was on track to complete more than 60,000 telemedicine visits for March 2020, up from 3,400 visits/month before the pandemic.)[1]
2. Telemedicine is cost effective for the patient and highly convenient—with an average wait time of just four minutes.
3. The technology is quite functional, including e-prescribing, downloading/uploading pertinent images, and using best-practice guidelines, for example.
4. Physical contact and potential contagions are avoided but the personal touch, interestingly enough, is still preserved.
5. It addresses overuse, misuse, and underuse of healthcare dollars by instituting standardization and consistency, the lack of which has led to a monumental waste of resources ($1 trillion per year).[2]

---

[1] David Cutler, PhD, et al., "The Business of Medicine in the Era of Covid-19," *JAMA* (May 1, 2020).
[2] Jackie Kimmell, "The 7 key factors driving $1 trillion in wasteful health care spending," Advisory Board (October 25, 2019), https://www.advisory.com/daily-briefing/2019/10/25/ihi.

6. People desire quick results with solutions that put a premium on their time, interests, and quality of life.
7. Telemedicine sets the stage beautifully for full practice transformation. See Figure 1 below.
8. It's the perfect conduit for sharing best practices and new ideas more effectively.
9. It creates a platform for dovetailing a number of other innovative initiatives outlined in this book.

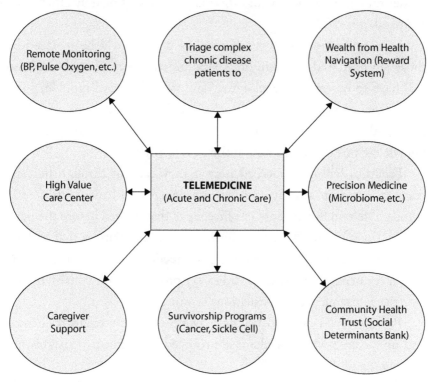

Figure 1: Telemedicine Platform.

What has changed?

Employers are primarily concerned with where one can get their best work done. Healthcare institutions are employers, as well as providers, and, without a doubt, face-to-face interactions through telemedicine have exploded and will become an expanding fixture from now on. Our society has suffered greatly from isolation and so much more so since the pandemic. Face-to-face interactions arranged in a few minutes have proven to be a godsend and are certainly amenable to effective diagnostic and management reasonings. Though I am a firm believer in a good physical exam, Osler's advice that "a patient is telling you their diagnosis" is so very true in most cases. There is a need for increased responsiveness by clinical professionals to the community, especially the harder hit communities of color that are disproportionately affected by the pandemic.[3]

So many current systems of medical practice will be replaced by those administered by more pragmatic practitioners of medicine who will have to be creative, exploratory and geared toward problem solving to stay competitive. There is also a need for new career development paths for providers earnestly seeking fresh skill sets to apply their knowledge postpandemic and in the new normal.

Facilities will only succeed now if they can cut through bureaucracy to ramp up quickly and become deluged with new business at comparable reimbursements to office visits that existed before the pandemic. There is a need for long-term expansion initiatives that include new services and remote monitoring connections as well. A true public health connection and widespread safety protocols with consistent and effective consequences for violations is crucial.[4]

Providers will need to become "aware of supply chain resiliency" and understand where products are sourced to "gain early insight into shortages and disruptions."[5]

As far as the handling of the COVID-19 pandemic itself: "The crisis demanded a response that was swift, rational, and collective. There was

---

[3] Tracy Brower, "5 Predictions About How Coronavirus Will Change The Future of Work," *Forbes* (April 6, 2020).

[4] Ibid.

[5] Peter Antall, MD, *Modern Healthcare* (April 20, 2020).

no national plan—no coherent instructions at all; families, schools, and offices were left to decide on their own whether to shut down and take shelter. When test kits, masks, gowns, and ventilators were in desperately short supply, governors pleaded for them from the White House, which stalled and then called on private enterprise, which couldn't deliver. Civilians took out their sewing machines…"[6]

We are not a third-world country, my friends. Yet, we have been so consumed, even overwhelmed, by mediocrity in our healthcare that we continue to seek leadership from individuals who are devoid of goals or fresh ideas. Healthcare represents the epicenter of such tepid reactive rather than proactive bold steps!

Oliver Munday asks, "Do we trust our leaders and one another enough to summon a collective response to a mortal threat? Are we still capable of self-government? The reform of the Obama years, important as they were—in health care, financial regulation, green energy—had only palliative effects." He further points out that "the gross inequality of our healthcare system is evident in the sight of refrigerated trucks lined up outside public hospitals."[7] This was, is, and will always be unacceptable.

With over 50% of elective surgeries eliminated during the worst of the pandemic, it is safe to say that a percentage of those individuals will conclude that perhaps they weren't necessary in the first place or become so frustrated by the backlog they will abandon such surgeries altogether.

Additionally, millions of Americans who live from paycheck to paycheck (perhaps up to 78% of all Americans) will further eschew any healthcare, whatsoever, because their limited funds must go toward food, shelter, and utilities and not necessarily in that order.[8] Not to mention the already existing high deductibles that keep so many away from healthcare.

---

[6] Oliver Munday, "The Coronavirus Revealed America's Failures," *The Atlantic*, (June 2020).
[7] Ibid.
[8] Zack Friedman, "78% Of Workers Live Paycheck To Paycheck," *Forbes* (January 11, 2018).

Healthcare employment, despite the pleas for more providers, will be drastically squeezed as the traditional moneymaking enterprises have been broadly reduced; rural hospitals, small practices, and overall health-care jobs will undoubtedly fail due to markedly reduced revenues. Those left standing will need to consolidate and drive up prices while insurance provided by many "soon to be bankrupt" companies will go away.

Seniors in assisted living facilities and nursing homes are being decimated by COVID-19, which will lead to more seniors deciding to age in place rather than reside in these "petri dishes."

On the positive side, our experiences with COVID-19 will be responsible for requiring, not suggesting, the game-changing transformation in healthcare that so many of us have been clamoring for so long. Due to the length of this prolonged "time-out," coping behaviors will have become ingrained in our daily lives, challenging the status quo and demonstrating the silver linings.[9] That is true change. And I am not speaking of just how to *pay* for healthcare, but how to fundamentally *restructure* its delivery for decades to come. Residual social distancing, heightened fear of the unknown, and increased savings for future rainy days are just a few societal changes easy to predict. Others are also as predictable and important for the healthcare industry to keep in mind, but are by no means exhaustive:

1. **Telehealth and telemedicine** is engaging, well run, effective, and a significant answer to accessibility, cost, and navigation.
2. **Remote workforce**. It is clear that a significant number of patients can be seen by using video and phone consults from anywhere, including home-based offices. Though I have been espousing this for almost twenty years, it has taken a pandemic to make it a widespread phenomenon. The savings to the system will be astronomical, and the issue of access will soon dissipate for most people.

---

[9] Jonathan Manis, "There'll Be No 'Back to Normal' for Healthcare Once the Covid-19 Crisis is Over." *Modern Healthcare* (March 30, 2020).

3. **Social networking**, meaning the coming together of communities to help each other, is exactly what we have accomplished with our Wealth from Health Community Health Trust prior to the pandemic, offering a tremendous value.

4. **Progressive, real-time communication, coordination, and collaboration tools** enabled by increased Internet capacities, raise serious doubts about the overriding need for expensive brick-and-mortar facilities, the so-called "edifice complex."

5. **Remote clinical observation and disease management** make it clear that a large percentage of the 100 million Americans suffering from chronic disease(s) can be managed quite effectively remotely, making telemedicine and telehealth game changers. The complex patient with severe comorbidities will still be seen and followed in the office as appropriate.

6. **Medical intervention by exception.** The American people are learning that many of the complaints they typically brought to the attention of their providers can be self-managed, one positive by-product of the pandemic. However, we need to know whether more serious issues were not addressed due to the fear of contracting the virus at the office or emergency room.

7. **Self-service diagnostics and self-care.** The advantage of establishing testing sites and the ability to deliver diagnostics in this way will have tremendous long-term ramifications.

8. **Payment and reimbursement concessions.** Clearly, the government cannot continue to call for concessions only on the part of insurers, providers, etc. The issue of large deductibles will go away because this technology is so affordable.

9. **Artificial intelligence (AI) and informational chatbots** identify opportunities to integrate experiences of practicing physicians into the implementation of best practices—a natural for real-time studies.

10. **Predictive analytics and knowledge management** is an area of statistics that deals with extracting information from data and using it

to predict trends and behavioral patterns, such as through AI and predictive modeling. The new healthcare world will need to rely on these abilities more and more.

11. **Top-of-licensure clinical practice** simulates an all-hands-on-deck approach on a regular basis, asking each provider to perform all duties specific to their credentials and are kept busy by doing so. The number of patients utilizing this is huge, although seniors and caregiver utilization will need to be encouraged.

12. **Ubiquitous access.** The 24/7 availability, using present and future technologies, will lead to more relaxed statewide-only licensing.

13. **Cross-industry collaborations.** All aspects of healthcare delivery are not only on the table, but will need to show overall cost effectiveness and utility in new models.

14. **Innovative care models.** Reengineering how care is delivered, by whom, and where is fundamental to this transformation.

Unlike the HIV epidemic of the 1980s, today's scourge is worse, in many ways, due to the ease of transmission through respiratory droplets that can also remain viable on inanimate objects. Frankly, the COVID-19 social distancing is more complicated than for HIV, which centered on sexual activity, protection, or abstinence in high-risk populations, including intravenous drug users. Furthermore, COVID-19 appears to be able to create permanent pulmonary scarring and death. (The eradication of HIV in a patient is another issue altogether.)

Additionally, we have heard, at the time of this writing, that the economic effects of the coronavirus pandemic on Americans includes mass joblessness, widespread bankruptcy, tarnished credit, and so forth: an Armageddon the likes of which we have never seen before. Although many experts agree we will emerge from this deep, deep quagmire a battered and bruised society, but, hopefully, wiser.

The Republican view to "trust the markets" for eliciting change hasn't worked well during the COVID-19 pandemic and never works in a crisis. The healthcare field has long been in crisis, and the pandemic has simply made it worse and more glaring. Joseph Stiglitz, the 2001 recipient of the Nobel Prize for economics, states: "We've been running our entire society without spare tires and proud of the seeming efficiency we have gained. And never prouder than in the healthcare sector. After all, this is part of how we can give huge profits to the health insurance and pharmaceutical companies."[10]

In a crowded world of 7.8 billion people, where the environmental issues are not seriously being addressed and no global public health mechanism is truly apparent, it should not be much of a surprise that obscure animal viruses are now a clear and present danger to human beings. The list: SARS, MERS, COVID-19, H5N1, H7N9, HIV, Ebola, arenaviruses, Nipah, Chikungunya, and Zika … is just the beginning. There will be others. The human species takes millions of years to effect a single species mutation, whereas these viruses do so in just a few days. How can we win against them? We must do better. There remains no other path or alternative; we must rise to the occasion now. Cartoonist Walt Kelly quipped years ago: "We have met the enemy, and he is us."

We can, for the first time in my nearly seventy years on the planet, define a new normal before the marketers define it for us. Get rid of the bullshit, and only bring back what works for us, what makes our lives more meaningful, what makes our children safer, and what makes us proud.

We start by determining:

- How we choose to spend our family time on nights and weekends;
- What we watch;
- What we listen to;
- What we eat;
- What we choose to spend money on;

---

[10] Joseph Stiglitz, "The View :The Markets are Failing Us," *Time* (April 20, 2020).

- Which local community efforts we support;
- Which organizations we support;
- What truths we tell and gravitate to those leaders who tell them;
- What events are worth attending;
- Who we give power to;
- What we will sacrifice for cleaner air;
- What choices must we make if we want a simpler life; and
- What effort are we willing to put toward fixing a fractured health-care system.

When our beloved country figures out the best times to "reopen" different businesses and events, we will undoubtedly hear: "Can't wait to get back to normal," or "I want to feel normal again." Julio Vincent Gambuto in his article *Prepare for the Ultimate Gaslighting* stated: "Every brand in America will come to your rescue, dear consumer, to help take away that darkness and get life back to the way it was before the crisis…. find the consumer's problem and fix it with your product. Brilliant marketers know how to rewire your heart."[11]

Please believe me when I categorically state: *This is not the case with the Wealth from Health initiatives we describe herein.* Especially since we are very much aware of how our individual and collective hearts have been traumatized and that we are so very vulnerable as a society, not to mention all the other countries ravaged to different degrees by this insidious virus.

Americans are now disheartened, scared, and yes, depressed. Let's look at some other facts that have surfaced during the prolonged "time out period." Only 400 people own more wealth than 150 million people.[12] The air over Los Angeles has been much cleaner without as many cars

---

[11] Julio Vincent Gambuto, "Prepare for the Ultimate Gaslighting," *Medium* (April 10, 2020).

[12] Mary Papenfuss, "400 Richest Americans Own More Than 150 Million Of The Nation's Poorest: Study," HuffPost (February 11, 2019) https://www.huffpost.com/entry/400-richest-own-more-than-150-million-poorest_n_5c60f627e4b0eec79b250c34.

that it is almost unrecognizable. Our healthcare system, touted as the best in the world, cannot provide basic protective equipment for its front line. Small and even large businesses do not have enough cash on hand to pay their employees or their rent. CNN reported that, as of June 4, 2020, nearly 43 million Americans have filed for unemployment benefits during the pandemic.[13] A government that has claimed credibility issues concerning our media means that 300 million people don't know who to go to for the necessary facts to save their families and their own lives.

That we are a nation with large, disquieting problems is clear. However, our busy lives often don't give us the time to think about anything other than making a living, looking at our computers/smartphones, and sleeping. But we *do* care about each other when we allow ourselves to feel. Most white Americans care very much about the plight of black Americans; most men do care about women's rights; most human beings do care about the environment; and most policemen care about the communities they serve. And yes, healthcare professionals do care about their patients' welfare.

As Jamie Ducharme of *Time* magazine points out her article "COVID-19 Is Largely Sparing Kids. Doctors Are Stumped" on April 6, 2020: "The gulf between people who can and cannot afford to seek out good care will become even more apparent. The country's most vulnerable populations…are the least likely to stock up on groceries and hunker down inside, less likely to have the means to safely travel to a doctor's office or can afford to work from home." Many work in service-focused jobs that puts them at increased risk for infection. The gap will undoubtedly widen as "the unemployment rate rises and individuals will have less access to health insurance. If healthcare is in high

---

[13] Anneken Tappe, "Nearly 43 million Americans have filed for unemployment benefits during the pandemic," CNN Business (June 4, 2020) https://www.cnn.com/2020/06/04/economy/unemployment-benefits-coronavirus/index.html.

demand and short supply, wealth will play an increasingly ugly role in it," continued Ducharme.

When the smoke clears after the worst of this pandemic, I feel quite certain that our country will have changed and learned a great deal. People will have gotten used to a new economy in which doing without in some areas will have become habitual (i.e., shopping online for groceries). New healthcare interventions (i.e., rapid, randomized clinical trials and telemedicine services) will become the rule. Working from home, rather than renting expensive office space may become the norm as businesses see how efficient this shift will be. What better time to promote a true health equity and the substantial changes outlined here "while the iron is hot"? After all, we see what speed and alacrity can be achieved when a crisis emerges.

Lastly, one of the untold effects of this pandemic is the disastrous effects of loneliness and isolation on so many people forced into lockdown alone. Many decades ago, I remember attending a Jim Fixx symposium on heart health. Jim Fixx was a famous marathon runner who had been a long-time smoker before stopping and taking up running. (Unfortunately, he had sowed the seeds of coronary artery disease before seeing the light and died of a heart attack at only fifty-two).

His son continued his legacy with this conference in his name, and one of the lecturers dealt with the effects of fear, loneliness, and grief on the heart, which can lead to sudden death from heart failure. The syndrome was later identified as "Takotsubo syndrome," of which I have seen many patients whose stressful situations led to an outpouring of catecholamines (commonly known as epinephrine or adrenaline and norepinephrine or noradrenaline) into their systems. These chemicals, subsequently, cause a spasm of the coronary arteries that lead to major heart dysfunction and, in some cases, death. So when an elderly patient loses a spouse, it is not altogether unusual for the living spouse to pass away soon thereafter, presumably from loneliness and grief (a so-called "broken heart") that represents this syndrome.

That is why the Wealth from Health navigation system (discussed in later chapters) is so valuable both now and in the future. One of the most consistent messages from our over 4,000 participating patients is that they "did not feel alone" in handling the over fifty different healthcare and social determinant tasks confronting them. By the way, managers of programs like Lifeline can attest to the fact that the overwhelming number of calls are from individuals, mostly elderly, who just want someone to talk to and do not have any current acute problem.

While hospitals have, traditionally, centered their business models around inpatient services, the coronavirus pandemic has shown us that while they are great places for the truly sick people, other locales and professionals will suffice for many others without a downturn in results. We must be ready and embrace this *new normal.* To quote Bob Dylan: "The times they are a changin".

Douglas Ratner, MD

CHAPTER ONE

THE WEALTH FROM HEALTH MOVEMENT

T he Wealth from Health (WfH) formula includes a wide span of comprehensive initiatives designed to establish a true road map to meeting the needs of patients with value, which is defined as *melding quality and efficiency*. The formula relies on proven templates of change, rather than theoretical ones. Healthcare professionals traditionally run from "theory" to "how" after being convinced of the "why."

Wealth from Health is different because it is not theoretical. We have tested and revised all the initiatives in a large, multicultural and socioeconomically diverse urban population. We also have not relied primarily on nursing professionals (high compensation), community advocates (low skills), or phone follow-ups (low capture) to champion and implement the initiatives. WfH has sparked a *movement*, comprised of a unique "professional friend" model of college-educated salespeople who are skilled in developing trust and engagement. The patients come first.

Hospitals and physicians need to expand their offerings and see themselves, not just as *providers* of "sick care," but as *champions* of maintaining health. And the care delivered must also change rapidly and radically, proactively promoting good health habits beginning in childhood. I must be unafraid to upset the status quo, make experimentation central to our actions, creatively connect things, observe our patients like an anthropologist would, and finally, harvest what we have learned. This is the Wealth from Health formula and movement toward positive change.

Health systems will generate membership by understanding their consumers and offering a deeper relationship that builds value over time. The current business model is good at diagnosing disease and ending with prescribing a course of therapy; however, it is dying a natural death due to failure to show consistent benefit to the patient or society. The new model, outlined in this book, with evidence of financial and health success, can most effectively help patients adhere to the recommended therapies and make the behavioral adjustments necessary to live free from the complications of their disease(s). WfH is a comprehensive plan that can serve as a strategic vision for your healthcare system for the next three to five years post-pandemic. The twelve key strategies are:

1. **Wealth from Health Navigation Program.** This initiative is an incentive-based, credit-system methodology. It rewards patient self-management and ties into community businesses for attractive discounts and giveaways. A current business model that is good at diagnosing the disease and prescribing a course of therapy must morph into the model that can most effectively help patients adhere to that therapy and make effective behavioral adjustments. Staying connected to sterling WfH navigators, who have assisted over 4,000 patients to date, with up to 100 unique self-management activities necessary to live free from the complications of their diseases and are perfect for video chats/visits. Credits earned are rewarded by gift cards.

2. **Precision Medicine.** This term refers to the fact that we finally have (and will continue to have) an ever better emerging database that represents a huge leap forward in understanding why people get sick and ways to prevent those illnesses. Why certain people succumbed to the coronavirus, while others did not, is a great

example (correlations between age and certain serious preexisting conditions). Plus, by merging the socioeconomic and genomic information on each patient, we will finally uncover the issues that can accurately produce new therapies.

- *CRISPR:* (clustered regularly interspaced short palindromic repeats) is a gene editing technique.
- *Gene Therapy:* adding genetic material to cells to address abnormalities.
- *Microbiome Sequencing:* analyzing the genetic material of the bacteria, fungi, and viruses, etc. that live on and in one's body.
- *Whole Genome Sequencing:* replace select gene analysis.

3. **High-Value Care Center (HVCC).** To have any hope in competing on price, hospitals and health systems must address the root causes for their runaway price structure. Issues of overuse, misuse, and underuse along with diagnostic errors must be met head-on. A huge percentage of medical issues can be managed remotely with efficiency and help eliminate the $1 trillion of systemic waste mentioned earlier. Predictive analytics and knowledge management are the key and core features of these centers. A game changer.

4. **Primary Care Transformation.** Video/smartphone consultations will stand alongside office visits with office visits recommended only when necessary. The emerging standard for accessibility will provide seamless care that extends beyond physical access to care sites. COVID-19 has hammered this fact home. Virtual visits must take a seat at the table, starting with the fields of behavioral health and postacute care (the period after hospitalization) where reinvention is so critical.

5. **Reengineered Projects**. Innovation for the sake of your customers' health through offering affordable, reliable, and accessible products that meet discrete customer needs, such as the Race to Zero—a symptom-reduction program to make patients comfortable during the last two years of life—and the Environmental Housecall for

asthmatics to root out indoor pollutants, a major factor in the illness itself. Additionally, the Getting Stronger Program, the Help the Helper Program Financial stewardship, Behavioral Health Program, and other initiatives provide efficient and effective care and are the result of initiatives tested and proven in a large urban center.

6. **Diagnostic and Management Excellence Center.** This initiative utilizes newly created software and simulations to assist clinicians in developing a solid differential diagnosis and make "diagnostic reasoning" a vital core function in their daily routines. Also, acknowledging "management reasoning" as a separate learned skill set. Just by looking at this pandemic, one can readily see a hodgepodge of management reasoning decisions that, in many cases, defy reason and coincide with "medical intervention by exception" practices.

7. **Pharmaceuticals Affordability Initiative.** The cost of pharmaceuticals is also unsustainable for a significant segment of the population, the elderly, take many medications at one time and are on a fixed income. Faced with buying food and paying rent, guess which necessity is ignored? When, not if, antivirals and vaccines for COVID-19 are studied and tested appropriately, costs will need to be addressed to ensure compliance and accessibility.

8. **Healthcare Leadership and Innovation Initiative.** We must train our healthcare students and residents, leaders of tomorrow, now to become "change agents." *If not now, when?* we ask.

9. **Value Analysis Committee.** Establishing a business case based on cost-effectiveness must supersede political and hierarchical considerations when purchasing expensive equipment or electing to use expensive therapies. The use of ventilators—instead of the latest robotic surgery options, for example—is an eye opener in this pandemic. This includes self-service applications and self-service diagnostics.

10. **Cancer Survivorship, HIV Survivorship, and Sickle Cell Survivorship.** For the millions of Americans in which cancer has been

relegated to the status of a chronic disease, as HIV and sickle cell disease have, navigating these individuals through the rest of their lives will require trained professionals who look to coordinate care for these unique patients.

11. **Community Health Trust**. Communities must establish their population priorities according to the social determinants of health and then match the communities' resources in order to level the playing field. A perfect formula that leaves no one behind as we speak of transportation, access to fruits and vegetables, legal advice, and so forth. Thoughtful collaboration by corporate, philanthropic, education and government as well as social networking is the key.

12. **Financial Care Stewardship.** Considering our patients' finances must no longer be ignored. Structuring a method by which a physician can advise and share expense information prior to ordering procedures, medications, etc., while seeking effective alternatives, must be established. If fee for service (FFS) remains, make it cost-effective and transparent as in telehealth promulgation.

The Wealth from Health Paradox

"What is the Wealth from Health paradox?" you might ask. The dictionary defines the word "wealth" as "an abundance of valuable possessions or money." In fact, most definitions refer to material entities. However, we firmly believe that good health makes one truly wealthy, because without it, life is exceedingly difficult, if not lamentable. Furthermore, we cannot measure up as a society unless we come to the realization that every life matters; being poor or uneducated does not make one less important in this world. Stating the obvious: we are all God's children.

After a solid month of social distancing, New York City officials noted that Hispanics averaged 22 deaths from COVID-19 per 100,000, Blacks 20 per 100,000, Whites 10 per 100,000 and Asians only 8 per

100,000. The obvious evidence of health inequality this pandemic has revealed remains a perfect storm. The gap will, undoubtedly, widen as the unemployment rates rise and individuals will have less access to health insurance. If healthcare is in high demand and the supply is short, personal wealth (or lack thereof) will play an increasingly ugly role in obtaining it.

In a perfect world, we would hope that all individuals involved in the healthcare delivery system—insurers, hospital CEOs, pharmaceutical companies, etc.—provide value and have the patients' best interests at heart. However, my four decades in healthcare informs me otherwise. Many of them have economic goals from the start, which you might say are not irrelevant to good outcomes. However, as the waste in the gargantuan American healthcare system is fast approaching $1 trillion per annum in a $3.6 trillion per year industry,[14] the time for change is now. Objective data conclusively proves that more healthcare does *not* always translate into better healthcare, regardless of some who claim otherwise.

The insurance companies have always wanted to insure healthier people because they save on payouts and the majority of the premiums stay in their coffers. The fact that the people they want to insure are healthier is a business move, short and to the point. The insurers steadfastly refused to cover preexisting conditions until Obamacare shoved it down their throats and gave them an ultimatum in 2014.

On the other hand, the CEOs of hospitals need sick patients because that is their business model; their jobs have depended on filling beds … as long as patients do not wear out their welcome. That is, diagnosis-related groups (DRGs are the present system of reimbursement) pay better if you grace their doors but don't stay long. Simply put, profits are limited by beds that don't turnover fast enough. Perverse? You betcha.

---

[14] Jackie Kimmell, "The 7 key factors driving $1 trillion in wasteful health care spending," Advisory Board (October 25, 2019), https://www.advisory.com/daily-briefing/2019/10/25/ihi.

Physicians, however, know that due to the dangerous microorganisms existing in hospitals, less time means less exposure, hopefully. I can assure you that this fact is not on the radar of most CEOs though. One ambitiously driven CEO explained why he refused to consider backing the WfH disease-management initiatives: "They will keep fannies out of my beds." Outrageous? Yes, but I am certain he is not an outlier in this misplaced belief.

Others will reason, "No money, no mission." I would submit and have done so to their faces: "Since when does doing the right thing for our patients take a back seat? Doesn't that sound like a cop-out?" In fact, innovative CEOs are always trying to recognize new streams of income to stay afloat while serving their patients. They are necessary businesses, after all. However, only some are undertaking capitated risk, in which a system's revenue is not tied to intensity of care but rather to efficient, effective care. The majority of CEOs do not because their efforts to make people truly healthier lag woefully behind their profit center: treating the sick. It is simply too difficult to do so profitably.

Some CEOs will throw some real money to fund an onsite farmer's market, while others will come up with "wellness" efforts that pay lip service to the concept, but do not reach the individuals who need these programs the most. Incidentally, although this may sound overly cynical, and you may be prematurely concluding that this author represents just another disenchanted physician, you needn't worry. After this eye-opening chapter, you will spend the remaining time on tested and proven, positive, game changing efforts that can help fix this broken system.

I am aware of a hospital in Illinois that offered their services at a markedly discounted rate, only to be overrun by consumers who had previously eschewed healthcare due to the exorbitant prices. The hospital had simply not done the necessary work (over time) to prepare for a new paradigm of care. I submit, however, that if the Walmarts, the

Amazons, and so forth can figure it out, why can't we do so with a new breed of enterprising CEOs?

As far as the pharmaceutical industry is concerned, their profit motives are out there for all to see: drugs that cost $100,000 per year and, in many cases, much more. Is there any wonder why healthcare costs are the leading cause of personal bankruptcy in the United States?[15]

Federally Qualified Health Centers and the Underinsured

My career in medicine spans four decades and, following long stints as a Chairman of Medicine in two healthcare institutions, I have seen and participated in many healthcare activities that have been inspirational, heartbreaking, instructive, and, lastly, illustrative. Throughout most of that time, I have maintained a close relationship with my patients and, in fact, am spending my semiretirement taking care of patients at a Federally Qualified Health Center (FQHC) in Asbury Park, New Jersey.

For those unfamiliar with FQHCs, there are about 9,000 of these ambulatory sites in the United States that care for all comers regardless of ability to pay: uninsured individuals and those on Medicaid, an insurance most of my professional colleagues refuse to accept due to its meager reimbursement, are the majority of patients. These centers rely on grant dollars, insurance, and sliding scales (income-based fees) for payments. This is our country's best attempt to deal with health inequity, but time and time again, when I've found myself confronted with a complicated patient whose medical management superseded my ability to be "all things to all people," I reached out to a subspecialist

---

[15] Laurie Konish, "This is the real reason most Americans file for bankruptcy," CNBC.com, February 11, 2019. https://www.cnbc.com/2019/02/11/this-is-the-real-reason-most-americans-file-for-bankruptcy.html.

for guidance and failed to receive it. I sought their expertise in invasive procedures, such as cardiac catheterization, gastrointestinal endoscopy or colonoscopy, and pulmonary bronchoscopy … to name a few of the skills beyond my expertise as an internist. Over the decades I might add, either through my teaching of over 500 residents, or from sheer necessity, I have learned to be rather self-reliant. Consequently, I only reach out, in my opinion, when absolutely necessary. Recently, a bright, well-educated Caucasian woman, age fifty-nine, came to see me after having undergone a repair of a thoracic aortic aneurysm and a coronary artery bypass operation. These are two substantial surgeries, which if not carried out, would have imperiled her life. Her clinical state was precarious. She was single and supported herself, but further troubles awaited her as she lost her executive position in a marketing company due to the excessive amount of sick days she'd been forced to take, even though her previous absenteeism from work was nil. Accordingly, she now qualified for Medicaid or as some cynics would say, "add hypoinsurancemia" (an oft-mentioned term to describe the "wrong" type of patient, one with insurance deemed subpar) to her burgeoning list of problems.

She described her initial care as "optimal and respectful" until her insurance situation changed. At which point, the providers she encountered appeared "disinterested, dismissive, and condescending." Even my attempts to speak with her cardiologist, after noting some additional worrisome findings in her physical exam and electrocardiogram, were ignored. I was informed by the practice that only the physician assistant would honor her insurance but her cardiologists "would not." Speaking to this physician assistant, who was congenial, proved inadequate because his knowledge level prevented a more in-depth discussion. I politely asked for the on-call cardiologist there to call me, but no one did. Subsequently, my patient ended up in the emergency room with another heart attack. Even my calls to the hospital's ER physician and medical floor hospitalist proved fruitless, as neither one returned my call.

To put this in perspective: perhaps owing to my previous position as Chair of Medicine and a practicing internist for many patients with private insurance prior to my new FQHC position, my calls had always been returned immediately. My patient tearfully recounted that her hospital physicians "didn't want to be bothered." I mention her case for two important reasons. First, she was white but low income, or designated "poor." And I point this out because minorities have experienced this phenomenon for decades (our dirty little secret). Second—and I affirm this with all the energy I can muster—being "poor" seemed to make her less desirable as a human being and less worthy of respect or an empathic response as those with better insurance. In fact, over the years, I developed my own system to combat such despicable human behavior on the part of many of my medical brethren. Surgeons or subspecialists who agreed to see my poorer patients would also be sent my privately insured patients, ignoring any call lists that dictated otherwise.

David Blumenthal, president of the Commonwealth Fund, contends that: "Racism in the United States has been and remains pervasive, and overcoming it requires daily efforts to recognize its influence and counteract it." Furthermore, "This is tough and uncomfortable work, especially for the many dedicated healthcare leaders and professionals who deeply believe that they are personally unbiased, and provide compassionate, high quality care to all their patients. I was one of those."[16]

K. Sivashanker, MD, MPH wrote: "Our systems have been constructed, usually unintentionally, to deliver outcomes that vary according to factors such as patients' skin color or their ability to pay for services. ... there is a troubling lack of urgency over stratifying data. Such hesitancy may come from the common but misguided belief that

---

[16] Jonathan Manis, "Transformation in Healthcare Is an Imperative; We Just Aren't Sure What We Want to Become," *Modern Healthcare* (January 20, 2020).

clinicians are 'colorblind' and that race or other characteristics don't effect care."[17]

Much has been written about the poorer and uneducated patients who do not even possess the knowledge or willingness to speak up and totally rely on the advice and guidance of their providers. However, I have taken care of many well-educated, affluent patients who often approach their physicians in the same way, assuming the so-called "sick role," an almost childlike regression of parent and child. To these individuals, physicians must assume a "protector" role, of sorts, by treating them as we would demand of providers treating our own family members.

This last sentence is key, and for those providers to whom this lament doesn't apply, I salute you. But for those who have fallen down here, you'll need to do some serious soul searching. Excusing oneself due to a formidable schedule, the vagaries of electronic medical records (EMR), or simply the emerging healthcare landscape that seems to limit one's independence, is often used. But it's clear that these practitioners have migrated too far from the heady days of medical school and training when our idealism enveloped us. Then we were bathed in "doing good" instead of "doing well." Incidentally, no one drove expensive cars, wore designer clothes, or went on exorbitant vacations back then. We were all of one class: poor due to school loans, with not enough sleep, and thankful for the little things: a hot meal, an occasional Sunday off to sleep late, and, if we were lucky, some sporting event.

Bottom line: We are all human beings, aren't we? We bleed the same, mourn the same losses, and wish to be happy and contented as we go through this life—which I fear is in a less than empathetic world. Perhaps dismissing the feelings of others deemed "less than" has been rampant among us and just been given the license for open expression by the behavior of our politicians, but I think it's been around forever.

[17] K. Sivashanker, MD, MPH, et al., "Advancing Safety and Equity Together," *NEJM* 382;4 (January 23, 2020).

A Truly Broken System

The prejudices and dismissive attitudes on the part of many healthcare providers and healthcare institutions do not cease once we leave the world of the disenfranchised. There has been a devaluation of what a life represents by many whose single-minded goal is to recapture or maintain their comfortable lifestyle, despite diminishing reimbursements.

A urologist, a surgical subspecialist whom I know well, was scheduled to implant a device to help a diabetic patient achieve an erection. An important procedure for this male of seventy years or so, though an elective one, meaning there was no emergent nature to the surgery. Prior to his being brought to the operating room, his patient began to complain of severe "chest pressure" that appeared cardiac in nature. The urologist, consumed by his desire to complete his allotted surgeries during his surgical time slot, wanted to complete the surgery, but was worried. Cancelled surgery represents a considerable loss of income because all surgeons are given slots on the operating room schedule and cannot just choose a time, unless there is a surgical emergency.

He asked one of my internal medicine residents what to do after hearing his patient's complaint. He was instructed to request an EKG and troponin assay immediately to determine whether any cardiac damage had occurred to the heart muscle itself. Even so, the surgery should have been cancelled right away and the patient admitted directly to the step-down unit or cardiac care unit—or failing that, brought to the emergency room. Without waiting for the results of those tests, however, he chose to proceed and performed the surgery, somehow convincing the anesthesiologist to ignore the complaints as well and proceed. Incidentally, anesthesia—despite the concerning protestations at the subsequent Peer Review (a hospital committee to examine possible substandard care)—had never questioned the patient beforehand of the presence of chest discomfort or exercise intolerance. The patient had a cardiac arrest (his heart stopped beating) during this elective procedure that could have been avoided.

To compound his egregious behavior, once the patient was revived, the surgeon continued the surgery. Needless to say, he cardiac arrested again and, miraculously ,was successfully resuscitated a second time, but sustained significant heart damage. The Peer Review committee, of which I was a member, heard the case but other than a mild slap on the wrist, failed to sanction this practitioner, who had a number of additional negligent cases on his record, or revoke his hospital privileges. Why? Urologists are few, and the committee chose not to pursue a path that could lead to his ouster. Also, the Chief of Surgery at the time had sustained his own cases that resulted in bad outcomes, and I'm afraid that chastising a colleague when your own professional work remains under question is simply not done. I am certain that the patient never understood the negligence inherent is his "care." In fact, direct from the famed Surgeon General himself, Dr. Edward Koop's speeches, "Most cases of medical malpractice that are filed are not malpractice, while most true malpractice cases are never filed." Contemplate that. The uninformed simply do not question untoward results like they should.

Furthermore, healthcare institutions often talk a great game and yet, they do not wish to attract the nonpaying customers to their doors or support physicians who are not huge revenue generators regardless of the community's needs. The worst offenders are the emerging institutions, the "for profit" hospitals, that have sprung up around the nation. Groups of businessmen and women gobble up distressed hospitals with a poor payer mix and half-filled beds, while those who occupy many of the beds are "hypoinsurancemiac." Neighborhoods fearful of being left without a nearby hospital are suddenly buoyed by the prospect of their hospital(s) staying in business.

In New Jersey, certain for-profit hospitals were able to raise the prices on patients with private insurance to obscenely high amounts, knowing that the insurers had to pay such outrageous fees if the patients were admitted through the emergency room. So all patients were funneled there; direct admissions became a thing of the past.[18] One case even garnered front page headlines when the parents of an uninsured boy who received four sutures for a small laceration in the ER were billed $17,000, the "acceptable" price they would have charged the insurer. This came about when the NJ legislature ruled emergencies had to be seen, and if no negotiated contract existed with insurers, the hospital could charge the higher price, and the insurers must pay it. Of course, negotiating with the insurers for a fair price was not high on the list for these hospitals. To further test the systems' mission ourselves, we decided to schedule an imaginary uninsured patient for a mammogram after claiming she had a large, suspicious mass that was clearly palpable. We were given an appointment for fourteen months in the future. Fourteen months! Outrageous.

Some would say that our "market-based culture" is to blame here. I am trying hard not to think of this term as a euphemistic attempt to conceal a more damaging one. "Lay understandings of culture usually focus on norms, values, interactions, and beliefs."[19] Many social anthropologists view culture not as a fixed state but as an ever-changing and conflict-ridden process."[20] We do appreciate that healthcare professionals feel uplifted when they, or their organizations, succeed in helping individuals lead more productive lives and have a healthy bottom line. So let us recognize that we must, once again, endeavor to level the playing field and erase a culture that many providers and healthcare organizations pay lip service to, yet their hearts aren't really in it.

---

[18] Adam Andrzejewski, "Top U.S. 'Non-Profit' Hospitals & CEOs Are Racking Up Huge Profits," *Forbes* (June 16, 2019).

[19] Michael Norok, M.B., et al., "Transforming Culture in Health Care." *NEJM* 381;22 (November 28, 2019).

[20] A.P. Cheater, "Managing culture en route to socialism: the problem of culture 'answering back,'" *Zambezia* XVI:103–22 (1989).

CHAPTER TWO

FIXING PRESENT-DAY HEALTHCARE

O n January 19, 2012, the Eastman Kodak Company filed for Chapter 11 protection in U.S. bankruptcy court because it was late to absorb the fact that it was not in the film and camera business. It was in the imaging business.

Beginning in 1973, Xerox's Palo Alto Research Center developed numerous breakthroughs in personal computer technology, including a graphical user interface, mouse, and laser printing. But perceiving itself as primarily an office-copier business, Xerox never brought this research to market. Apple did and sold 70,000 units in the first 100 days.

But some organizations have learned not to box themselves. CVS Health, which operates drugstores and pharmacy benefit programs, along with the insurer Aetna, are looking to merge, as they see themselves poised to deliver a holistic approach to health: leveraging CVS's approximately 10,000 drugstores into healthcare hubs for Aetna's subscribers. "It aims to be the new front door to healthcare in America."[21]

Also, Amazon, Berkshire Hathaway, and JP Morgan Chase have announced their intention to enter the healthcare arena. This frenzy of mergers and additional alliances is occurring at a feverish pace. Why? Simply put, to attract and capture patients as revenue sources, while healthcare providers remain somewhat intractable in refusing to fix

[21] Leemore S. Dafny, PhD, "Does CVS-Aetna Spell the End of Business as Usual?" *NEJM* 378, 7 (February 15, 2018).

their own houses. And patients are learning about choices by becoming active players in their own care: using walk-in clinics, urgent care centers, and cell phone apps to post a rash or find their blood sugar numbers. They are looking for convenience and lower cost, which is hard to find in an emergency room or spending hours in a physician's office. So battle lines are being drawn to see "who will control the patient, and who will capture their hearts." For physicians and hospital systems the choice is clear: reinvent or risk a debacle like Kodak or Xerox. They will need to expand their offerings and become champions of maintaining health. Care must rapidly and radically change.

Currently, healthcare metrics and reimbursement systems do not reward results that matter to patients and their families. We need to run from the aforementioned "edifice complex" (building larger, more complex, and often redundant buildings and systems) mentality, rework the outcome metric system (toward rewarding value), and phase out fee for service over the next three to five years. Moving to a community-based business by attacking social determinant deficits, adopting virtual visits, involving businesses in healthy community efforts and concentrating on navigating 100 million chronic disease sufferers will require innovatation.

Present-day offerings presumed to be of consistently high quality are not, and science can now define high- versus low-value care. Low-value care wastes trillions of dollars per year due to the overuse, misuse, and underuse of healthcare dollars. Reversing this waste must be addressed immediately and systematically and should be tied to reimbursement systems that reward results that matter to patients. Let's begin paying for what works: personalized healthcare in several forms—the coming together of precision medicine and population health (discussed later in greater detail). And it's not just the dollars; the current U.S. healthcare system has left us thirty-seventh in the world for quality health outcomes.

"It does not take much imagination to see the clear and unmistakable parallel of the military industrial complex" that President Eisenhower warned against to the similarly developing "medical-industrial complex," as city, state, and federal governments have paid the private sector to deliver healthcare just as it utilized private industry to develop our military might.[22]

To repeat, we as physicians must lead the move from a product-oriented business (clinic visits and procedures) to a community-based one that addresses the social determinants of health, prioritizes outpatient settings and virtual care, and wisely navigates and coordinates the over 100 million patients with chronic conditions in the United States. If we abdicate this responsibility, business leaders and financial institutions will continue to fill the void, creating a model that serves everyone *except* the patients.

Additional markets for the Wealth from Health formula approach to healthcare delivery will be employers, concerned consumers (the patients and their families), governmental officials, and academics who are seeking to understand the how and why of the high-resources/poor-outcomes system that now defines the American healthcare industry. Why does it exist and, most paramount, how it can be fixed now by proven templates of change?

Why do we believe this formula will work? Because as physician/authors, we are not theoretical. We are working, executive-level physicians and have tested and revised initiatives in large multicultural and socioeconomically diverse urban populations. We also have not relied exclusively on old, inadequate patterns: using nursing professionals (high compensation), community advocates (low skills), or phone follow-ups (low capture) to reach patients as they navigate complex care.

---

[22] A.S. Relman, "The New Medical-Industrial Complex," *NEJM* 303 (October 23, 1980).

For these programs, navigation is provided by a unique concept of the "professional friend": college-educated salespeople who are skilled in trust and engagement. And we add to this the wise use of healthcare resources and our population health concept of a Community Health Trust, which is a diverse group of stakeholders and governmental departments who can match resources to patient needs and identify social determinant shortfalls by using our own stratification tools, thus leveling the playing field for our patients and families. We can demonstrate the concept that good business and humanity need not be mutually exclusive. The Wealth from Health Navigation Program is designed to help healthcare systems meet today's priorities.

First, let us reaffirm that the most basic and fundamental relationship for healing and nurturing good health is that of the patient-physician.

Second, it is absolutely paramount to enable physicians to spend adequate time with patients who need extra time: those with diagnostic uncertainty, those with failed treatment plans, those at the end of life, and those who require true coordination because they are seeing multiple subspecialists. Accordingly, clarifying the diagnosis and treatment plan helps the patient make important decisions about next steps.

Third, one's access to care, its affordability, and lack of opportunities for physician innovation are additional failings in the current system and must be remedied.

Fourth, the issues of opioid addiction, gun violence, maternal mortality, childhood education, and healthy nutrition are crucial to the health of all communities.

Fifth, most physicians struggle to use poorly designed technology that diminishes their enjoyment in their work, while spending more and more work on clerical duties.[23]

---

[23] John Noseworthy, MD, "The Future of Care-Preserving the Patient-Physician Relationship," *NEJM* 381;23 (December 5, 2019).

Who Would Benefit from Reading This Book?

Physicians and Healthcare Providers: We need to take a hard, honest look at where we presently find ourselves and what efforts need to be mounted to fix our house. By addressing the myths and detailing proven solutions, there can be only one conclusion: we *can* collectively fix our issues going forward. Physician leaders need to emerge quickly!

Government/Insurers: The federal government needs to analyze and repair the noted short comings of the Affordable Care Act, regardless of its future as a mandated program. This includes a focus on regulation of the pharmaceutical industry and tort reform which comprise 7% to 8% waste respectively.

Policy/Lawmakers: This book will provide a detailed map for government and private insurers to gravitate toward rooting out waste and reducing clinical variation.

Employers: Caring employers will realize that the healthcare industry has heard their clarion call for the industry to finally wage war on the significant wastage and mounting unsustainable costs in the system.

Consumers/Patients: This all-important group will understand that there are now evidence-based guidelines (the ABIM Foundation's Choosing Wisely™ campaign, for example), where they can go to reference many tests that their providers may recommend, and they can match recommendations against the scientific evidence. Healthy lifestyle choices and each family member's self-management discipline will need to be adopted in order to be in control of their health destinies. Working with incentive plans, like the Wealth from Health rewards program, in their own homes to promote such choices among family members is paramount. They will be able to seek out healthcare systems that actively cultivate community involvement and resources to model mitigating those social determinants of health that prevent an even playing field for good health.

Academics: This group will be necessary to change metrics for healthcare professionals so that creativity and innovation become hardwired into education. Another market, and one becoming increasingly popular at our institution, is professional students (medical, nursing, pharmacy), who are looking to understand the landscape of reform.

Current Issues

The issue of our time is security, both health and economic. Many would argue that healthcare affordability affects both, rendering our present-day society pleading for solutions to where the Affordable Care Act has fallen short, and our government is seemingly helpless to effect the type of change needed. Only those in the healthcare trenches know where to go to fix what is broken, and truly change our business proposition from producing healthcare to achieving health. This is what people want, and they are just beginning to look at the power they can wield as every healthcare system in the United States desperately fights for every patient. Their competitors are not just other health systems, but also insurers and the CVSs, Amazons, etc. of this world. The fee-for-service reimbursement model will have to end because it is unsustainable as the government itself seeks models of care that make sense.

Many of the leading healthcare best sellers have played a role in creating thoughtful dialogue, but many, certainly not all, fall short in the following ways:

- They only touch on one or two problem areas. The need is to comprehensively direct attention to a span of initiatives (the twelve pillars of Wealth from Health, for example) that are wide ranging. A piecemeal approach to healthcare at this time is counterproductive because these areas are crying out for reengineering and represent an interlocking mosaic.

- Relying on theory, often based on other industries—which in itself is not necessarily bad—but after identifying the problem, they supply generalities instead of proven templates. We have already created and tested our initiatives in real time. Only a few books are able to lay claim to this fact. Healthcare professionals generally run from "theory" to "how" after being convinced of the "why."
- Relying on scare tactics or pounding the profession mercilessly without issuing a reproducible road map to change what doesn't work. Perhaps that is a sign of the times, but it's not helpful. After all, my fellow healthcare providers are, for the most part, wonderfully gifted and compassionate human beings.

CHAPTER THREE

LIVING UP TO DONALD BERWICK'S VISION OF THE "TRIPLE AIM" (QUALITY, COST, AND CARE)

> "It is always better to define a business by what consumers want than by what a company can produce."
>
> —Theodore Levitt, the editor of the
> *Harvard Business Review* in 1960

Thomas Robert Malthus once stated that population naturally tends to grow "geometrically," and, in a finite world, this means that the per-capita share of the world's goods must steadily decrease. Barring the expansion of the human population to the far reaches of Mars, (my brother-in-law and world-renowned expert on Mars, Dr. Robert Zubrin, would love to see this), the world is finite. So is the money spent on healthcare. Yet, Americans are just waking up to this thought as they are asked to shoulder more and more of the cost. What is the origin of this misconception?

The tendency is to assume that decisions reached individually, in fact, represent the best decisions for an entire society. Adam Smith's *The Wealth of Nations* (1776) describes the "invisible," which came to mean that "an individual who intends only his own gain is led by an invisible hand to promote the public interest." Nonsense. In fact, a mathematician by the name of William Forster Lloyd wrote in 1833 about the "Tragedy of the Commons,"[24] which occurs like this: "Picture a pasture open to all. It is to be expected that each herdsman try to keep as many cattle as possible on the Commons. Such an arrangement works reasonably satisfactorily for centuries because tribal wars and disease keep the numbers of both man and beast well below the carrying capacity of the land. ... Finally comes the day of reckoning, the day when the long desired goal of social stability becomes a reality. At this point, the inherent logic of the Commons remorselessly generates tragedy."

In other words, the rational herdsman concludes that the only sensible course for him to pursue is adding another animal to his herd. And another and another, a conclusion, by the way, every other rational herdsman arrives at, as well. Each man is locked into a system that compels him to increases his herd without limit in a world that is truly limited. "Ruin is the destination toward which all men rush, each pursuing his best interest in a society that believes in the freedom of the Commons."[25] Freedom in the Commons brings ruin to all.

I wish to thank Donald Berwick, MD, founder of the Institute for Healthcare Improvement and former administrator of the Centers of Medicare and Medicaid under President Obama, who in his book *Promising Care*[26] alerted me to that 1968 article in *Science*, which I read in total. Folks, the healthcare dollar is indeed finite, and as we go forward here, keep the "Tragedy of the Commons" and the lesson it teaches in your thoughts; you may even consider reading the original article yourself. Furthermore, when you read about the Community Health Trust we created, you will see how this concept has never been more topical or timely.

---

[24] Garett Hardin, "The Tragedy of the Commons," *Science* (December 12, 1968).
[25] Ibid.
[26] Donald M. Berwick, *Promising Care: How We Can Rescue Health Care by Improving It* (San Francisco: Jossey-Bass, 2014) 180–184.

In *Promising Care* Dr. Berwick cleverly points out the following: "Healthcare does not need everything it can get, not by a long shot, not if what it's trying to do is give us the three things we need: comfort, answers, and longer years of good health." He concludes with this statement: "The healthcare system that gave us each what we really, really want would be, it can be, a system sustainable for our futures and for children's futures. But it would be different from the one we have."

A few years ago, the Obama administration began to veer away from the term "healthcare reform" and instead talked about "health insurance reform"—a big difference, which is lost among all the politicos or others who like to ponder these issues. Essentially, the reform would be either to spend more or help less. Who knows what will be cobbled together after all the self-interested groups have their ways with the proposed legislation or redo of the Affordable Care Act? Dr. Berwick also raises this question in his excellent read: "How could Congress possibly know enough to specify for every community, the exact design so that: care is safe, effective, patient centered, timely, efficient, equitable?"[27] Exactly. I wouldn't presume to tell a carpenter how to put a deck in or an electrician how to wire a house to code. Not that all providers will be equally adept at becoming "change agents." Similarly, I hired a carpenter to hang a door once, and he proceeded to put the hole for the doorknob on the wrong side. Or when I hired an electrician to find a "short" in our house's electrical system that took him all day (he was paid by the hour) to trace it to an old lamp that my wife had insisted we keep, much to my chagrin. In effect, that was an $800 lamp after the electrician finished his not-too-timely search.

To our readers, please understand that we should strive for the very least healthcare that we need to achieve a life full of joy and *nachas*, a Yiddish word for good things to happen, so that at the end one can say, "It has been a life well lived."

---

[27] Ibid.

Other Berwickian principles include:

- Healthcare training, particularly that of doctors, is predicated on a belief in trained perfectibility. *A nonsensical goal; I couldn't agree more.*
- Healthcare activities are among the most error-provoking on the planet. *Sad, but true.*
- Embrace citizenship and the greater whole that is healthcare, even when caring for a single patient. *So true.*
- Cooperation, teamwork, inquiry, and dialogue are key skills to know. *So necessary.*
- How to find answers is more important than knowing answers. *Engineers have been saying this for years.*
- Embrace the authority of patients and a wholly new distribution of power. *Providers, are you listening?*
- Willingness to trade prerogative for reliability. *Coming down from the pedestal does not diminish us in the slightest.*
- Assumption of expertise, altruism, and self- scrutiny characterize a professional in medicine. *Do we want to do good or simply financially well?*
- Best predictor of cost is more; the more we make the more we use. *Human nature?*
- There is no relationship, whatsoever, between the quality and outcomes of care with the supply and use of healthcare. *A restatement of the previous point.*
- Accountability is as fragmented as care itself. *Yes, indeed, rampant in so many professions.*
- It is fundamentally immoral for health insurance companies' main goal is to sell health insurance to people who are not likely to need healthcare. *Certain four letter words come to mind.*
- Good healthcare funding must be just, equitable, civilized, and humane. *Social determinants.*

- Avoid supply driven care like the plague. *Must end for the system to right itself.*
- Don't put your faith in market-driven forces. *A cop-out indeed.*
- Aim for health. *Amen.*

Are you following so far? I hope so.

The "Less Is More" Argument

As many know, those of us who argue "less is more" when it comes to healthcare, point to a body of research, much of it from The Dartmouth Atlas Project , that there is little correlation between higher spending and higher-quality care.[28] We agree that this may represent an oversimplification, but simply put, no one has ever looked at the risks posed by *not* knowing a diagnosis. In addition, this concept fails to take into consideration the relationship between outcomes and a physician's expertise. In other words, there are examples when evidence says *no*, but an experience doctor may say *yes*. The clinical feel sometimes goes against the most likely. Still, the data does lead us to the correct conclusion that doing more is not a predictor of successful health outcomes.

The United States has a daunting challenge. Among all of the high-income countries, we have the sickest and highest mortality population of all.[29] In fact, the rate of death from conditions that can be managed and treated effectively (referred to as "mortality amenable to healthcare") is also far higher than other high-income countries.[30] Outrageous, no? Even so, patients with chronic illness spend only a few

---

[28] The Dartmouth Atlas Project, "Accountable Care" (updated 2018). http://www.dartmouthatlas.org/keyissues/issue.aspx?con=2943.

[29] Eric Schneider, MD and David Squires, MA, "From Last to First: Could the U.S. Health Care System Become the Best in the World?" *NEJM* 377.10 (September 7, 2017).

[30] Lisa, Rosenbaum, MD. "The Less is More Crusade: Are We Overmedicalizing or Oversimplifying?" *NEJM* 377.24 (December 14, 2017).

hours a year with a provider but "over 5,000 waking hours each year engaged in everything else … all the time making choices about activities that can profoundly affect their health."[31] Taking medications, following medical advice, what to eat and drink, whether to smoke, and so forth. The solution? Effective navigation, which we will discuss in the Wealth from Health navigation section of the book.

Seeing patients over the past thirty-plus years also has taught me this caveat: many times we physicians are (simply put) unsettled about uncertainty. Many instances of testing and diagnostic procedures demonstrate a hunger for information, rather than a desire for financial gain. The reality remains that doctors continually have to make decisions based on imperfect data and limited available knowledge.

In 1817 the poet John Keats, who was a physician, wrote to his brothers: "At once it struck me what quality went to form a man of achievement … when a man is capable of being in uncertainties, mysteries, doubts, without any irritable reaching after fact and fiction."[32] However, we run the risk of premature closure by trying to achieve certainty too soon and thus produce diagnostic uncertainty,[33] which we will deal with later in the book. Have I got you thinking?

But will technology save the day? It will not allow the providers to restore their lost sense of professional satisfaction that can only come from an effort to bring about a renaissance in medicine, where a "sense of teamwork, community, and the ties that bind us all together as human beings," once again dominate.[34] Can we get there? Let's explore.

---

[31] David A. Asch, MD, MBA, et al., "Automated Hovering in Health Care: Watching Over the 5,000 Hours." *NEJM* 367:1 (July 5, 2012).

[32] Cameron Conway, "Negative Capability Press," https://www.cameronconaway.com/negative-capability-press/.

[33] Arabella L Simpkin, B.M., B.Ch., M.M.Sc., et al., "Tolerating Uncertainty-the Next Medical Revolution?" *NEJM* 375.18 (November 3, 2016).

[34] David I. Rosenthal, MD et al., "Meaning and Nature of Physician's Work." *NEJM* 375.19 (November 10, 2016).

Issues we must address:

1. Can better measures of quality outcomes be established in order to revamp reimbursement for office and telemedicine visits and hospitalizations?
2. Will we then redirect finances toward these outcomes?
3. Will primary care physicians or subspecialists, for that matter, utilize mobile apps and remote monitoring to transform their traditional practices into a new healthcare delivery system?
4. Will all the stakeholders become better stewards of their system's finite resources?
5. What alternatives to the present education of medical students, medical research, health policy, and reimbursement will be taken?
6. How best will the American Board of Internal Medicine's Choosing Wisely™ campaign be adopted by all stakeholders?
7. Will doctors and hospitals start focusing on what people really want, which is health, rather than just producing healthcare?
8. Will providers understand that social circumstances are just as important—or maybe even more so—than biologic processes in determining one's health?

Just some of the issues.

CHAPTER FOUR

LAYING THE GROUNDWORK

I recall listening to a healthcare lecturer describe the difference in administrative costs (before the Affordable Care Act) between government-run Medicare and private insurers amounting to roughly $485 billion. His point was that the government was far more efficient administratively than private insurers in this regard; he emphatically stated that such savings would have been able to cover a majority of those currently uninsured. Surely, no one would argue the benefit of Medicare for the American population. Also, it is estimated that over $1 trillion of our $3.2 trillion healthcare budget (at last count) is wasted due to overuse, misuse, underuse, and diagnostic errors in the healthcare field. While some would argue less, even so, there is no question that many of those dollars could be put to better use. As a tax-paying individual and physician integrally involved in the healthcare field, this obscenity must stop!

My colleagues and I have spent the past dozen years or so, and many of us much longer than that, attempting to do just that, but most importantly, we've been creating templates for change, such as the Wealth for Health initiatives already developed, put into use, and undergoing as rigorous an evaluation within the constraints of manpower we have. The phrase "return on investment" always lurks in the background and fuels a constant battle with CEOs, CFOs, and COOs.

This is understandable since the C-suite looks for security in their positions and report to a board of directors who must be concerned with financial viability.

I would like to think the central reason is that the field of population health is a relatively new one, and the American medical field is just beginning to factor in the importance of social issues. My more cynical side believes, though, that somehow these issues conjure up images of the welfare state to many, thereby pitting liberals versus conservatives, the haves and the have-nots, the haters and the believers, and so forth. I and my team are only interested in making a difference in all our patients' lives. People bleed the same blood, agonize over family illnesses in the same ways, hope to get through a day without significant pain, and provide the best for their children.

In fact, those of us who work in safety-net hospitals understand all too well the importance of social determinants. During extremely cold months, we have significant difficulty discharging patients to homes where there is minimal heating or in some cases none. We arrange for free nutritional counseling at our grocery chain, Shoprite, along with discounted fruits and vegetables offered to our Wealth from Health members—which, in many cases, represents the first time anyone has taken the time to plan out the benefits of such foods. "The role of social determinants of health, and the business case for addressing them, is immediately clear when it comes to homelessness and housing. The 1.5 million Americans who experience homelessness in any given year face numerous health risks and are disproportionately represented among the highest users of costly hospital-based acute care.[35]

To fix America's healthcare system, we must be willing to look at everything we do and examine the evidence, even for the time-honored annual physical, and let the chips fall where they may. I bring up the

---

[35] J. Michael McGiniss, MD, MA, MPP, et al., "System Strategies for Health Throughout the Life Course." *JAMA* 316.6 (October 25, 2016).

issue of annual physicals because they comprise 10% of the annual healthcare budget, although whether they are cost effective has been put in serious doubt.[36] Those who are in favor point to the healing power of the personal connection between patient and physician, of which I can professionally attest. I was keenly aware that many patients enjoyed the opportunity to converse with—and yes connect as—human beings. However, a very wise person once said to me, "Change is always viewed as loss."

But sometimes when we look back at the origin of customs or actions handed down from one generation to the next, to our surprise and sometimes chagrin, we find no basis in fact for that practice. For example, in healthcare, the ten days of antibiotics was the rule for many years, and the 10g of hemoglobin (the protein that carries oxygen in our blood) remains the gold standard in that we transfused individuals whose hemoglobin fell below this number. Neither meets scientific rigor. I think you get the point. It is crucial to integrate clinically meaningful measurements into care delivery at the correct points of interaction based on real evidence.

But this is not enough. We need to improve our processes. Over a decade ago, Kaiser Permanente California decided to improve their members' blood pressure control rates. They developed treatment algorithms integrated into their workflows—a registry enabling real-time tracking and real feedback to their physicians, while involving pharmacists and nurses and promoting fixed-dose combination drugs. Furthermore, they began "drop in blood pressure visits" with no copayments among other changes. They subsequently achieved blood pressure control rates exceeding 85%, an increase of over 35%.[37]

---

[36] Ateev Mehrotra, M.D., M.P.H., and Allan Prochazka, M.D., "Improving Value in Health Care—Against the Annual Physical," *NEJM* 373.16 (October 15, 2015).

[37] Elizabeth A. McGlynn, PhD, et al., "The Quest to Improve Quality—Measurement is Necessary but Not Sufficient," *JAMA* (October 17, 2016).

Wealth for Health Measures

Assessing and mitigating barriers of social determinants—such as lack of transportation, the need for legal advice, sound housing, good eating habits, access to fruits and vegetables, and so forth—and our creation of the Community Health Trust to finally involve the community in a meaningful and tangible way helps level the playing field for those seeking better health. Additionally, we have constructed a stratification tool that we employ for each patient to aid the provider in taking these issues into account.

We have tackled the issues of overuse, misuse, and underuse by creating a High-Value Care Center whose function is to rollout evidence-based treatments and procedures into the clinical world in a speedy way.

We developed a program to address the myriad of issues that confront our patients and their families that are never talked about, but still factor deeply and profoundly in-between doctor visits, hospitalizations, and health-seeking inquiries. The program was aptly named Wealth from Health because we truly feel that protecting the health of our family members and ourselves truly constitutes a wealthy, successful life—one in which we are able to pursue the joys of our family and friends and in one's employment. The incentive-based credit system works beautifully and also serves as a community business-marketing drive par excellence in that it directs traffic to stores and websites for prearranged discounts by the respective businesses, rewarding patients for each self-management step taken.

Clearly, the primary care practice of today needs to undergo a major transformation in order to deliver the type of care that make sense, is accessible and affordable, and provides the patient with what they seek from their vantage point. We predict the use of the smartphone as a major contributor in this effort is the era of what we call "Precision Medicine meets Population Health" to produce what others have termed "personomics" or "panoramic medicine," meaning highly individualized patient care. More on this later in the book.

Certainly, we must note the fact that tens of millions of Americans will survive their initial bouts with cancer, but unless they are overseen (traditionally called a cancer survivorship program), they may succumb to further comorbidities at a higher rate than individuals who've yet to be confronted with cancer. Hence the Wealth from Health Cancer Survivorship program and the Getting Stronger program.

We attempt to do better than the "lip service" the medical professions gives to end-of-life care. Since much of one's healthcare dollars are spent in the last few years of life, and most people choose comfort over longevity when given the choice, we've created the Race to Zero program, whose goal is simply to manage symptoms referable to all diseases. Understanding that we will never live forever, most human beings hope to make those last few years comfortable and remain with their families and friends, even if there is no cure in sight.

We strive to improving diagnostic excellence on the part of our physicians by developing software that aids clinicians at the *beginning* of the diagnostic process, which can lead to tremendous morbidity and mortality and yes, higher costs if not handled properly. Hence the DOCASSIST.AI software.

Providers must become stewards of their patients' finances as it applies to their healthcare and no longer remain above the fray. So we've created a Financial Stewardship effort, as well as instituted a Value-Analysis Committee, whose purpose is to require providers to furnish a business plan before requesting expensive technology, etc.

Pediatric asthma has long been a major issue, especially in urban areas, and our Pediatric Asthma program utilizes a home visit to root out environmental toxins. Furthermore, we outfit the home with dust-mite-killing formulations, as well as hypoallergenic pillowcase covers, mattress covers, etc. and educate the homeowner on how to reduce or eliminate indoor pollutants. The program is appropriately entitled the Environmental Housecall™ program.

Health disparities are found in age, education, race, ethnicity, sex, sexual orientation, and place of residence. Only focusing attention on creative ways to reduce social disadvantages can reduce health inequalities, hence a Community Health Trust like ours was borne.

One of the benefits of being responsible for delivering healthcare to people of every ethnic group and educational level is realizing that there is far more in the human condition that we share than issues or qualities that divide us. Poverty can afflict all races. Now, we all have heard said that "We picked ourselves up by the bootstraps, why can't they (the poor, black, Hispanics, etc.)?" Would it surprise you to know that one half of all African-Americans are defined as middle class or upper class?[38] Now, the 25% who are poor is a real issue, but I will leave these discussions to others. As a physician, my only concern is for the health of my patients. As an author, however, we must avert the Tragedy of the Commons.

We hope that you will appreciate and contemplate the naked truths and initiatives we introduce in this book, understanding that we do not wish to rail against our colleagues and healthcare systems we are immersed in, but rather begin the effort that will lead to every human being in this country enjoying good health.

Staring at the earlier list of Wealth from Health initiatives can be quite daunting, especially to those institutions that are just beginning to grapple with the issues at hand. We advise you to take one or two initiatives, concentrate on them first and, remember that it is never too late to start. Be cognizant of the central premise that revamping the healthcare system must not represent rearranging the chairs on the Titanic, but rather means building a newer, leaner healthcare system that echoes the words of Mark Twain: "Always do right. This will gratify some people and astonish the rest." Additionally, "Policies that attempt

---

[38] "The African American Population Report, First Edition," accessed February 14, 2017. www. black demographic.com.

to reengineer the health system without changing the underlying financial incentives that drive health spending will ultimately fail."[39] Cannot repeat this enough.

Beginning the process of putting this over $3 trillion dollar (and on its way to four) industry on the road of recovery will not be easy. In 2015, the U.S. population was currently hovering at around 320 million; according to the Centers for Medicare and Medicaid (CMS), the national healthcare expenditure was projected to $3.207 million that year. The per-capita amount spent continues to grow![40]

High-need, high-cost individuals, or the 5% who account for 50% of healthcare spending and whose complex conditions often render them unable to care for themselves, must be managed more effectively. There are those who feel that "we should go where the money is," to quote Willie Sutton when he was asked why he robbed banks. Those with complex diseases (the 5/50 club) deserve most of our attention, many would argue. Makes some sense, but what of those with two or more poorly managed chronic diseases (called the rising risk), the next wave to enter the 5/50 club unless significant intervention occurs with effective navigation. Reasonable people can disagree here as there is just so much money to go around.

Money again. Even a modicum of success in eliminating the waste previously discussed go a long way in eliminating or prolonging the ascension of the rising risk to the 5% who account for 50% of healthcare spending. Go where the return on investment (ROI) will be most forthcoming and/or take a more long-term view. We believe in both!

"Mural dyslexia—the inability to read the handwriting on the wall."

—Unknown

---

[39] Joseph Antos, PhD., et al., "Bending the Cost Curve Through Market-Based Incentives," *NEJM* 367.10 (September 6, 2012).

[40] D. Munro, "U.S. Healthcare Spending on Track to Hit $10,000 Per Person This Year," *Forbes/Pharma Healthcare* (January 4, 2015).

CHAPTER FIVE

INNOVATION IN HEALTHCARE DELIVERY SYSTEMS

Most individuals choose to work in the healthcare system to earn a living, but medical students gravitate toward this particular area due to a strong need to help their fellow human beings during the most vulnerable times in their lives. (I truly believe this.) However, any position can become mundane, even repetitive. The collective effort brought forth here offers new positions, imaginative ones, where individuals can freelance within a structured environment and so-called reinvent themselves. The ultimate goal is the making of the new healthcare system. Richard Bohmer points out, "Major change emerges from the aggregation of marginal gains. In practice, healthcare transformation is a long series of local experiments."[41]

Let's spend some time discussing how healthcare innovation occurs and why we believe its absence continues to be a major impediment to achieving fiscal responsibility and long-lasting healthcare quality. Some people choose to categorize innovation on the basis of whether it is disruptive or nondisruptive. *Nondisruptive* innovation refers to improving on something that already exists. One example is the Minute Clinic clinics, which are easily accessible, efficient, and cost effective, but do

---

[41] Richard Bohmer, M.J., MB, ChB, MPH, "The Hard Work of Health Care Transformation," *NEJM* 375.8 (August 25, 2016).

not replace existing medical facilities. *Disruptive* innovation creates "new players and new markets while marginalizing old ones,"[42] as they seek to deliver dramatic value to stakeholders. An example would be major industry leaders flying their employees across many states to a single site for hip replacement, deciding that value (meaning quality plus efficiency) covers the cost of flights and accommodations for the patients and families.

The ideas presented in this book will display qualities of both types of innovation. A preeminent example of an innovation carve out is 3M's "bootlegging" policy, under which all its technical staff are encouraged to spend up to 15% of their time working on projects of their own choosing. This practice has produced some of 3M's landmark products, including Scotch tape and Post-It Notes. Another example is our Navigational Rewards program discussed later in detail.

Perhaps, a better way to classify innovation would be the following:

Product innovation, meaning introducing a good or service that is new or significantly improved. A good example would be our Community Health Trust tied into a Stratification Tool, which delivers on the promise of leveling the playing field for patients and families from dire social environments.

Process innovation, meaning a new or significantly improved production or delivery method, such as our High-Value Care Center, which has the responsibility of delivering evidence-based information and hopefully, reduce clinical variation at the same time.

Marketing innovation, meaning a new marketing method with significant changes in product, design, packaging, placement, promotion, or price. A great example here would be the Wealth from Health incentive methodology.

Organizational innovation, meaning a new organizational method of a firm's business practices, workplace organization, or

---

[42] Clayton M. Christensen, et al., *The Innovators Prescription: A Disruptive Solution for Healthcare* (New York: McGraw Hill Education, 2008), 118–120.

external relations. An example here would be when the Jersey City Medical Center (JCMC) first joined the Barnabas Health System and, ultimately, the Robert Wood Johnson Barnabas Health System. Another would be the deemphasizing of the traditional bricks-and-mortar healthcare delivery systems to one that greatly emphasizes outpatient and virtual care.

Diffusion of innovations in healthcare remains a major challenge. Much of this has to do with answering the question: What is the catalyst for healthcare innovation? Not wishing to sound crude, but the old adage, "Follow the money," often becomes the only mantra. What the government does, and does not do, tends to drive this train. I recall the briefing of a few thousand healthcare executives by a top official in the Obama administration when the Affordable Care Act was first established. The official pointed out that he was being deluged by healthcare systems calling his office to inquire how they could get a their "hands on the money" being proposed, instead of trying to figure out a better way to deliver healthcare, get better results, and try to steer away from fee-for-service. The phrase, "necessity is the mother of invention," should resonate, don't you think? Another phenomenon is whether innovation chases need(s) or need(s) chase innovation? Again, the ideas presented in this book touch on both. That is, solutions looking for problems to solve first or problems in search of solutions to adopt.[43]

Healthcare organizations typically do not have the luxury of huge research and development departments, so they must rely on one the creativity of their work teams. That is exactly what happened at Jersey City Medical Center where the Wealth for Health team, composed of healthcare workers with different backgrounds, came in with one mission in mind. Innovation, innovation, innovation.

---

[43] Vincent K. Omachonu, et al., *The Innovation Journal: The Public Sector Innovation Journal* vol. 15.1, article 2, (2010).

Health-Information Technology Infrastructure

Let's face this central truth: a health-information technology infrastructure that facilitates monitoring, learning, and predicting the health status of individuals or populations would represent a significant step forward. We know that Silicon Valley is willing and ready to do so. There is no question that every corporation or individual who fancies themselves an entrepreneur desires to break into a $3.2 trillion dollar industry, healthcare. That is, any angle, any opening, whether well thought out or whimsical, has been attempted. After all, the allure of becoming the next billionaire "tech" guy abounds everywhere. For example, eye glasses for moderately demented individuals programmed to immediately recognize individuals' faces and flash their names in the upper corner, lest the familiar face go unnamed. However, Silicon Valley is deadly serious here and sees an opening for innovation. Most return on investments do not always revolve around cost per product (although, don't get me wrong, this business principle is still alive and well) as it does on reducing costs, though prices are often so steep as to discourage sales from the get go.

I'm reminded of the discussion I had years ago with the spouse of one of my residents in training in Internal Medicine, who was a top-tier computer savant for well-known computer giant. He was certain that computers would eventually replace providers and thought it ludicrous to entrust providers with the responsibility for mastering all the information in the medical domain. When we discuss use of the smart phone as envisioned by Dr. Eric Topol, one can conclude that he was partially right. There are more monthly visits to the WebMD network, a collection of health websites, than to all the doctors in the United States. Sixty million disagreements among eBay traders are resolved using "online dispute resolution" rather than lawyers and judges, which is three times the number of lawsuits filed each year in the entire U.S.

court system. In 2014, the IRS received almost 50 million electronic tax returns, relying on online tax preparation software rather than human tax professionals.[44]

The role of technology and medicine is a train that has left the station. There remains no doubt that mobile phones have penetrated the market like no other technology before. There are more than 5 billion wireless communications subscribers worldwide, and more than 70% of them are in the lower-middle income category. Additionally, commercial wireless signals reach 85% or more of the world's population, extending much farther than the electric grid. These numbers are too significant to ignore. "Engineers, healthcare professionals, economists, telecommunication professionals, and scientists need to get together"[45] to figure out how mobile technologies can truly revolutionize healthcare. One thing is sure, mobile health is here to stay.

Lastly, a driving mind-set of our Wealth from Health team was: Do not ask, "What do my customers want?" Rather ask, "What do my customers love?" Big difference.

---

[44] R. Susskind and D. Susskind, "Technology Will Replace the Doctors, Lawyers and Other Professionals," *Harvard Business Review* (October 11, 2016).

[45] Amira Roess, PhD., MPH, "The Promise, Growth, and the Reality of Mobile Health—Another Data Free Zone," *NEJM* 377.21 (November 23, 2017).

CHAPTER SIX

THE NEW DIMENSION CALLED "SOCIAL DETERMINANTS OF HEALTH" DELIVERY SYSTEMS

To really comprehend the relative importance of each social determinant of health (SDOH) to a particular individual, one must look at how difficult it is to explain the phenomena of health variation itself. One example would be the significant and speedy decline in cardiovascular and cerebrovascular mortality between 1970 and 1980. Clearly, a decade is too short a period of time for biologic (genomic) change, while some effect from decreasing smoking in men can be causal. However, female smoking did not decrease. Therefore, medical care was the most likely reason for the decrease—either the quantity or quality—including the state of science and technology.

And what about the sharp increase in life expectancy from 1940 to 1945? There was a .5% per annum increase during those years, which couldn't have represented a biologic or significant scientific or technologic change during such a short time. Also, 50% of the physicians went to war, so it wasn't medical care. Dr. Victor Fuchs pointed out that "social determinants, such as unusual increases in income, decreases in unemployment, and positive shifts in the national psyche inspired by war were the most likely explanations."[46] Fascinating stuff.

---

[46] Victor Fuchs, PhD, "Social Determinants of Health-Caveats and Nuances," *JAMA* 317.1 (January 3, 2017).

Before reading on, chew on this thought: the United States guarantees all citizens an education, access to fire and police services, a national postal service, military protection, a national park system, and so forth, but, inexplicably, no healthcare coverage. There still remain over 25 million Americans without health insurance.[47] Really? But this is much more than health-insurance status. Social determinants as barriers to healthcare have been a frequent topic in the literature.[48,49]

Some of the most pressing social determinant conditions in your community can include:

- Access to healthcare
- Cultural diversity, literacy
- Economic stability
- Environment
- Food security
- Food stamps\SNAP
- High school graduation rate
- Housing
- Literacy
- Mental health
- Nutritional awareness
- Poverty- line employment
- Seniors in poverty
- Social isolation
- Transportation
- Violence

[47] Howard Bauchner, MD, "Health Care in the United States: a right or a Privilege?" *JAMA* 317.1 (January 3, 2017).

[48] Christopher F. Koller, Alexander Thomas, and Susan Birch, "Population Health—a Bipartisan Agenda for the Incoming Administration from State Leaders," *NEJM* 376.3 (January 19, 2017).

[49] Arvin Garg, Renée Boynton-Jarrett, and Paul H. Dworkin, "Avoiding the Unintended Consequences of Screening for Social Determinants of Health," *JAMA* 316.8 (August 23, 2016).

Income and education, in fact, do affect one's entire life course. We know that higher incomes are related to better health outcomes, including less cardiovascular disease, diabetes, and depression, as well as a lower age-adjusted mortality. Examples of imaginative initiatives in America that address this issue include the earned income tax credit, giving 30 million low- to moderate-income working families cash transfers via federal EITC benefits. State benefit increases have been linked to better birth outcomes and better adult physical and mental health. Another, the federal Supplemental Nutrition Assistance Program (SNAP) targets approved diets for enrolled children and serves an estimated 45 million households, but it still misses approximately 17% of eligible participants. Programs that really are thriving are: We Care, Health Leads, Project Dulce, Safe Environment for Every Kid, and Help Me Grow. Lastly, on June 16, 2016, thirteen of Philadelphia's seventeen city council members voted *yes* on the city sweetened-drinks tax, marking the first time a large city in United States has done so.

In fact, eliminating health disparities in United States has climbed to the top of the national healthcare research agenda. It is the foundational goal of the federal Healthy People 2020, as it should be. "Family partnership address threats to social, emotional, and cognitive health for children of low-income families by assessing family needs, educating and supporting parents, and coordinating services. Maintaining health throughout life requires resources that enable healthy behaviors and reduce environmental risks. Cigarette smoking, lack for diet, contribute to well over 30 premature deaths, poor diet, contribute to well over 30 premature deaths. These risk factors, shaped by social economic forces, are more common among individuals in low social net economic groups. Life expectancy of 40-year-old man in the poorest 1% of the income distribution is 14.6 years shorter than for men and the richest 1%, and for women, the difference is 10.1 years."[50]

---

[50] Nancy Adler, PhD, et al., "Addressing Social Determinants of Health and Health Inequalities," *JAMA* 316.16 (October 25, 2016).

If we magically rid the American public of tobacco, sedentary life-styles, and alcohol, would chronic disease continue to account for 85% of our healthcare cost?[51] Perhaps, but not $3.2 trillion per year, which brings me to another topic.

Community Health Trusts

Community Health Trusts (CHT) can stratify your population, accord significant importance to the social determinants of health, and match with city's resources coalesced into a CHT in order to level the playing field. No handouts here, but a leg up. How have we in healthcare been so oblivious to the obvious for so many years? Why do most Western civilizations spend more money on social services than healthcare? How could we fail to see that an individual who has minimal access to heat, transportation, legal services, or fruits and vegetables could not follow instructions to purchase expensive medications when their basics are not in place? Let's get real!

In fact, one could argue that Community Health Trusts could determine which services have the greatest long-term value for their population and offer incentives for using them. Halforn and Conroy even suggest forming "health utilities" (meaning shared services and support) that will "improve horizontal integration and create community platforms for high-performing, networked health systems. Government, health plans, employers, providers ,and others could collaboratively fund mechanisms that support community health ..."[52] It is interesting to note that when I tried to explain the Community Health Trust concept to the senior leadership of JCMC, I did not receive much initial encouragement, but two years later, we made it happen. Leaders of tomorrow, be prepared for that type of initial reaction when introducing

---

[51] William Dietz, MD, PhD, et al., "Chronic Disease Prevention-Tobacco Avoidance, Physical Activity, and Nutrition for a Healthy Start," *JAMA* 316.16 (October 25, 2016).

[52] Neal Halfon, MD, MPH and Patrick Conroy, MD, "The Opportunities and Challenges of a Lifelong Health System," *NEJM* 368.17 (April 25, 2013).

something new. To make certain, you must present it all together, so as not to confuse the listeners.

Keep in mind that screening for social determinants can inform providers of adverse exposures and conditions that technically require resources outside of a traditional healthcare setting. That is why Community Health Trusts, like the Wealth from Health model, are so important. In fact, some would say that not identifying these needs and being unable to ensure referral and/or linkage would be unethical, a bridge to nowhere. Even the state-supported Legal Assistance to Medical Patients (LAMP) project has been able to help our patients by answering questions and providing solutions to such questions. Those critical questions include

- Have you been denied unemployment benefits?
- Is your child or are you disabled or not receiving disability benefits from Medicaid?
- Are bill collectors calling you?
- Have you been beaten or abused?
- Do you have problems with your landlord?
- Are you homeless?

With the help of member agencies of the CHT, resources made available for our members include: training for employment, free dietitian/nutritionist consults, linkages to primary care providers and specialists, help with obtaining health insurance, legal services, scholarships at the local schools, gym discounts, free supplies for back to school, free yoga and Zumba classes, assistance with SNAP, SSI, etc., and free nutritional counseling in our neighborhood ShopRite (a large grocery chain) stores with access to discounted fruits and vegetables.

These resources have been made possible due to the shared passion to improve the health of the population as well as the win-win nature for everyone. For example, by providing free navigation to children with asthma, the schools that participate in the CHT have seen a reduction in missed school days for the students. Parents who participate in the support groups have a decrease in missed workdays. School nurses have received in-services education and an Asthma-Friendly School certification, which has lessened their burden in documenting and providing in-school care for the children.

And these CHT schools remain critical for nutrition. Almost 22 million low-income children across the country receive free or reduced priced school meals. Publications from the National Academy of Medicine entitled "Nutrition Standards for Food in Schools and School Meals: Building Blocks for Healthy Children," provided the basis for the new standards for these programs, which includes more whole grains, a greater variety more fruits and vegetables, and foods with lower sodium content. These meals may be among the most and nutritious meals many children, including food-insecure households, consume. This says it all! Therefore, using patient navigation and shared community resources to find families at risk is an example of how barriers are reduced, allowing for healthier outcomes.

Accordingly, our medical students and residents need to rethink the social history (such as questions about travel, smoking, employment, etc.) that they query during their initial meeting with the patient. I'm reminded of one of William Osler's sayings: "The great physician treats the patient who has the disease, while a good physician treats the disease." For example, a social history should elicit key information:

- Life with arthritic knees and living in a third story walk-up and a violent neighborhood may make daily walks a serious challenge.
- Depression or poor coping skills make lifestyle modifications difficult.
- Limited mobility may hinder monthly visits to the pharmacy to pick up prescriptions.

- Social isolation may prompt excessive emotional eating.
- "Brittle" diabetic may reveal a very limited income that precludes purchasing healthy foods.

Possible solutions could include:

- Referrals to a food pantry and farmers' market;
- Referral to community-based walking programs where neighbors help one up and down stairs;
- Pharmacies that deliver;
- Medical/legal referrals from a safe house; and
- Community health centers for group meetings.

Learning to elicit a solid patient history is a skill that can be taught and does not require a clinical background. WfH navigators have developed a comprehensive tool (see page 52 Figure 2) that has been effective in both identifying and trending SDOH mitigation. This tool has been trialed and tweaked with the help of patients and families, as well as the input of the JCMC Community Health Trust described next.

An Effective Community Health Trust Prototype

An innovative Community Health Trust partnership with Jersey City government, advocates, social agencies, schools, and JCMC that pools assets and resources to create an infrastructure to support, manage, and expand activities to facilitate a healthy Hudson County, N.J. population has been accomplished. These partnerships and collaborations can be created in any community. Together, the CHT members can advocate for services that have the greatest long-term value for the population and offer incentives for using them. The partnership also provides a mechanism for connecting healthcare with social and public health services,

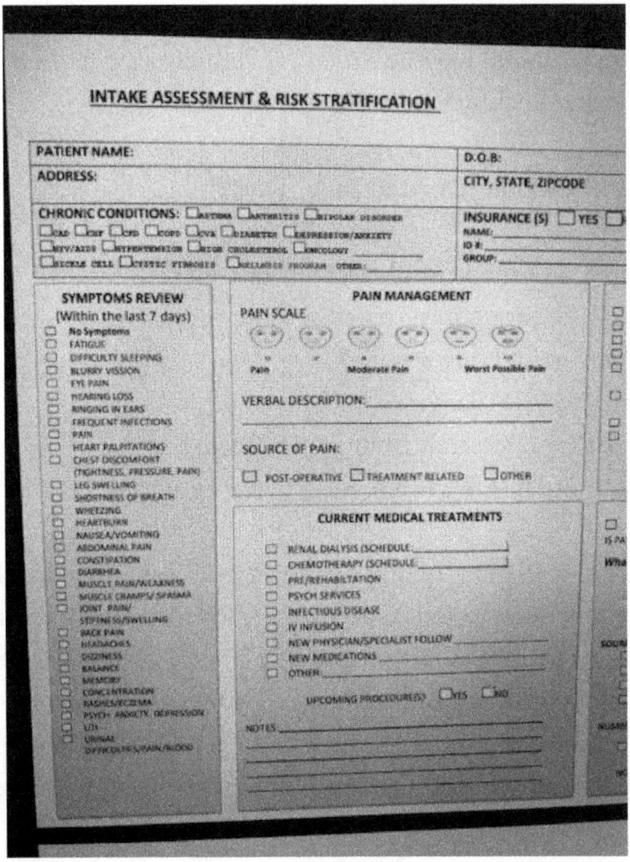

Figure 2: Page 1 of 4 of Intake Assessment and Risk Stratification Tool.

thereby enabling the formation of "health utilities" (meaning shared services and supports) that improve horizontal integration and create community platforms for high-performing, networked health systems.

The Hudson County Community Health Trust partnership holds quarterly review meetings in which all the existing partners and new partners are invited to a seminar to discuss ongoing projects, program scope and targeted populations, networking opportunities, and goal achievements. Partnership is embedded with contractual obligations from some partners and memoranda of understanding, formal agreements, voluntary arrangements, and informal agreements with others.

Currently over sixty community business in Hudson County have partnered with the hospital to provide various discounts to community members who agree to self-manage their chronic diseases. These businesses, some part of the CHT and some smaller vendors with a contractual relationship with Wealth from Health, Inc, include restaurants, gyms, spas, pharmacies, salons and others. All provide discounted services united around healthy choices.

To maintain this successful partnership, both formal discussions and communications with external partners are undertaken consistently. Per established communication protocols, monthly ongoing project update presentations are given to core internal and external stakeholders. These collaborative activities help promote and strengthen needed community partnerships and facilitate sustainable positive outcomes. The program staff has utilized these opportunities to conduct in-house training sessions, share resources, and program sponsorships throughout several organizations, including the public schools, federally qualified health centers, churches, and senior residential facilities in Hudson County, N.J.

When building a CHT, consider stakeholders such as social service providers, employers, education resources, health product manufactures, manufactures of personal digital devices, public health and safety organizations, quality assurance organizations, medical and communication agencies, finance and legal partners among many others as stewards of community organizations and resources, heretofore only fringe players in the healthcare field.

CHT Stakeholders

Whenever my house staff would complain about other care providers on the medical floors, I always responded with, "Everyone needs to feel like they have a piece of the rock (have their opinions heard)." It is pure conceit that would dictate otherwise. These stakeholders whose contributions have been barely acknowledged are, in many ways, more instrumental in giving patients and their loved ones more of what they want; bottom line. See Table 1 below for examples of community partners. Physicians need to get off their high horses and finally acknowledge what they should have years ago: we are all part of the same team but with different fields of expertise that can be melded into the optimal care unit.

Lastly, and perhaps the most controversial statement we can make, is that communities should have a strong voice as to where we earmark much of our healthcare dollars. Perhaps then, the United States will not lag so far behind other developed countries in social services spending. Furthermore, "Professionals and institutions would value social equity perhaps more keenly."[53]

Please do not underestimate the value of leveling the playing field, though I daresay that, if recreated throughout the United States, would not only greatly help those of the lower economic strata but indeed,

Table 1: Community Health Trust Stakeholders

REQUIRED PARTNERS (communities decide together additional members)	EXAMPLES
Academia	Dean/Provost medical school, universities. Superintendent public/charter schools
Corporations	Banking, major employers
Utilities	Electricity, gas, water, phone
Vendors	Local businesses
Government	City and county board of health, mayor representative
Community advocates	LGBTQ, Latino, immigrant representatives
Legal	Local attorneys. Legal aid
Social agencies	WIC, Medicaid, employment
Healthcare	Federally qualified health centers, schools of nursing, pharmacy, therapists.

---

[53] Jeremy Bey, PhD., et al., "Training the Workforce for 21st Century Science," *JAMA* 316.16 (October 25, 2016).

many of the middle class who also describe deficits in social determinants, as well as the wealthy who can afford to pay outside the system of care but have barriers around time and knowledge about what constitutes value care.

Wholistic Patient Care

Now that we are engaged in a healthcare battle required to provide care for all residents, eliminating the trillion dollar waste per year should rise to the forefront of all healthcare discussions. Through innovation, a health system should at the absolute minimum:

1. Support a High-Value Care Center (HVCC);
2. Redesign the curriculum and expectations for professional students and residents to better reflect healthcare delivery;
3. Create an innovative and effective patient navigation system that activates patients to self-manage their disease; and
4. Implement a Community Health Trust that promotes the sharing of already existing resources to obliterate the social determinant deficits that plague our system and reduce duplicity and waste in the system.

At this time, our country is looking for answers from governmental bureaucracy. I suggest that we stop this futile waste of energy. *The solutions must come from clinical leaders and through innovation.* Only by focusing attention on creative ways to reduce social disadvantages can we reduce health inequalities, such as:

*   Access to care
*   Access to fruits and vegetables
*   Community conditions
*   Diabetes

- Education
- Food security
- Housing
- Income
- Management of chronic illness
- Nutrition
- Safety
- Substance abuse
- Transportation
- Unemployment
- Violence

Some examples of resources that can come from Community Health Trust include:

- Assistance with SNAP, SSI, etc.
- Employment opportunities
- Job and interviewing skill development
- Free dietician/nutritionist consults at local supermarket
- Free back-to-school supplies
- Free yoga and Zumba classes
- Gym discounts
- Help with obtaining health insurance
- Linkages to primary care providers and specialists
- Scholarships at local schools

Wealth from Health Patient Navigation Program

At JCMC, patient navigators have been able to do more than just document barriers; they are charged with mitigating those barriers to improve health outcomes. Additionally, the program offers patients the ability to have a home visit and environmental health assessment—especially valuable for family members suffering from respiratory illnesses or at high risk for falls. Data gathered at the patient's home has been instrumental to clinicians as it allows the patient to be in a safe space, resulting in the discovery of information not usually discussed at the physician's office to best understand the patient's quality of life.[54,55,56]

The "informed friend" relationship developed between patients and nonclinical navigators allows patients to contact their navigators without fear of charge/copay or a long wait for response.[57] This relationship, along with patient incentives for meeting self-designed goals and healthy choices, facilitates patient engagement, which correlates with an improvement of health outcomes and decreases costs associated with inappropriate use of resources.[58,59] JCMC was able to show a five-year net positive ROI associated with decreased emergency room and inpatient stays of $5.2 million when comparing patients at twelve months of enrollment in the navigation program to the twelve-month period prior to enrollment—with 3,000 patients enrolled and seven patient navigators providing individual counseling.

A major tool that the patient navigators shared with patients and families to improve the continuum of care was a database of over 1,000 community resources through a partnership with the web-based service Aunt Bertha.[60] Furthermore, additional resources were provided by the members in the JCMC Community Health Trust.

---

[54] Kelly M. Doran, Elizabeth J. Misa, and Nirav R. Shah, "Housing as Health Care—New York's Boundary-Crossing Experiment." *NEJM* 369.25 (December 19, 2013).

[55] Arvin Garg, Brian Jack, and Barry Zuckerman, "Addressing the Social Determinants of Health Within the Patient-Centered Medical Home," *JAMA* 309.19 (October 11, 2013).

[56] Michael D. Rawlins, "Cost, Effectiveness, and Value," *JAMA* 316.14 (October 11, 2016).

[57] Sara Phillips, Narissa Nonzee, Laura Tom, Kara Murphy, Nadia Hajjar, Charito Bularzik, Xinqi Dong, and Melissa A. Simon, "Patient Navigators' Reflections on the Navigator-Patient Relationship," *Journal of Cancer Education* 29.2 (February 5, 2014).

[58] Erica S. Spatz, Harlan M. Krumholz, and Benjamin W. Moulton, "Prime Time for Shared Decision Making," *JAMA* 317.13 (April 4, 2017).

[59] Laurence F. Mcmahon, Renuka Tipirneni, and Vineet Chopra, "Health System Loyalty Programs," *JAMA* 315.9 (March 1, 2016).

[60] https://www.auntbertha.com.

CHAPTER SEVEN

IS HIGH-VALUE CARE THE HOLY GRAIL?

The healthcare battle of our time is not, contrary to public opinion, on fixing or repealing the Affordable Care Act. Instead, the real concern is the imminent need to wage war on the trillion dollar waste (30% of a $3.2+ trillion spent on healthcare) in healthcare delivery. The waste is a result of overuse, underuse, misuse, and diagnostic errors.[61] Numerous articles have been published that highlight the evolution of healthcare and the need to address concerns, such as social determinants of health (SDOH), medical education's failure to prepare physicians for transformation of care, and the need to foster innovation.[62] Unfortunately, there are few articles that discuss how to do so at one's institution.

David Grace, MD, a senior medical officer of the Schumacher Group, a large national physician staffing company, puts it simply: "A standard, consistent level of evidence-based information is essentially something other industries have figured out, but it's something that we in healthcare struggle with."

The need for insisting on high-value care practices is crucial, especially for the elderly who consume most of their lifetime share of healthcare dollars during their last two years of life. It is critical that we

---

[61] David Nash, MD, et al., *Demand Better: Revive Our Broken Healthcare System* (Bozeman, MT: Second River Healthcare Press, 2011).

[62] Donald M. Berwick, et al., "Breaking the Rules for Better Care," *JAMA* 317.21 (June 6, 2017).

get it right for these individuals and getting it right means giving them and their caregivers what they truly want, so mission critical.[63]

Financial return through lower cost per case is imperative in producing a pricing advantage in today's consumer-driven market. Let me say that again. *Achieving a lower cost per case is imperative in producing a pricing advantage in a consumer market.* A wonderful example that will illustrate the nuances of this issue involves antibiotic usage in the hospital. Infectious disease specialists are well aware of the ample data that indicates intravenous antibiotics need not be administered more than twenty-four to forty-eight hours after the patient has clinically improved. The arbitrary numbers of seven or ten days of antibiotics are unnecessary and even dangerous. This areas of waste (overuse) will surprise you, the lay person, and I daresay many physicians. Another example of overuse is in cancer treatment. Studies show that a large percentage of patients receiving chemotherapy or radiation for their cancers agreed to undergo such treatment because they believed it "would lead to a cure."[64] The provider either did not want to rob them of hope or, again, it is simply the case that to a carpenter everything looks like a nail?

We cannot overstate these points too much. With deductibles climbing through the stratosphere and hospital enterprises receiving less and less governmental subsidies and dollars, the issue of cuts to stay competitive or simply remaining solvent has never been more important. Case in point: Over the past few years, I and most of the administrative staff have sat through dozens of presentations given by consultants on how to save money. None of these highly priced consultants employ physicians with acute knowledge of (or the courage to) articulate the real "waste" issues of a trillion dollars nationally, but rather fixated on wringing out the dollars obvious to the naked eye,

---

[63] John Rowe, MD, et al., "Preparing for Better Health and Health Care for an Aging Population," *JAMA* 316.16 (October 25, 2016).

[64] Jane C. Weeks, M.D., Paul J. Catalano, Sc.D., Angel Cronin, M.S., et al., "Patients' Expectations about Effects of Chemotherapy for Advanced Cancer," *NEJM* 367 (October 25, 2012).

or the so-called "low-hanging fruit." Kind of like when a person hiking through a desert takes his shirt off and twists it ferociously to squeeze out the last remnants of sweat to drink. Perhaps extreme, but I think you get the point. But what if that same weary tracker was standing only feet above an underwater stream of flowing water, but didn't address the possibility of collecting that water to drink?

To accomplish this, each institution should develop their own high-value care center or participate in one owned by a consortium. Nothing wrong with sharing resources to accomplish this activity.

Wealth from Health High-Value Care Centers

To have any hope in competing on price, hospitals and health systems must address the root cause(s) of their pricing structure. Issues of overuse, misuses, and underuse, along with diagnostic errors, must be met head-on. It will not be effective enough to simply look at what the evidence demonstrates for a treatment, a procedure, or a process—all based on various studies—though that is an important first step. But there is a need to be creative in adopting new guidelines. After all, to demonstrate a good return on investment (ROI), one needs to prioritize *what* guideline, supported by evidence is an early change, or one could conceivably be caught attempting to "boil" the ocean here. (I'm accused of this, in any event, quite often). My colleagues and I have conceived of literally hundreds of initiatives, but using a Six Sigma methodology, we have categorized our efforts according the highest ROI. In this case, achieving some early wins will go a long way in convincing the powers that be of the soundness of such efforts.

And physicians must also quickly see the reason for change. When discussing issues of overuse or too much medical care, there are seven presumptions or reasons that seem to drive physicians to provide too much medical care. The reasons they fail include:

1. The inaccurate belief that all risks can be lowered (and that trying creates risks of its own).
2. Trying to eliminate a problem can be more dangerous than managing it.
3. Early diagnosis can needlessly turn people into patients.
4. Doing too much can scare patients and distract from what is important.
5. Action is not always the right choice.
6. New interventions are typically not well tested and often end up being judged ineffective and even harmful.
7. A fixation on preventing death may diminish life itself.

Trust me, any practicing physician reading this list can think of at least one example for each point that would substantiate it.

Other industries have been able to reduce waste and inefficiency by being creative and incorporating methodologies such as Lean Six Sigma and Agile. But it can be done in healthcare by using these or other models of rapid improvement. This chapter highlights how an urban safety-net hospital in Jersey City, N.J. was able to reduce waste and inefficient use of resources by:

1. Redesigning both graduate medical education and post graduate education through the framework of a High-Value Care Center (HVCC) which provides a new generation of physicians with the tools required to assess, test, and improve delivery of care and
2. Embedding a national award-winning patient navigation program into care redesign can enhance care coordination outside the confinements of the hospital walls and teach our patients the difference between high-value and low-value care options.

Issues of overuse are addressed nationally by the American Board of Internal Medicine Foundation's Choosing Wisely, the Centers for

Medicare and Medicaid Services (CMS) bundled-payment programs, and several other specialties' stewardship guidelines that are focused on right-sizing diagnostics and procedures. These efforts work to broadly decrease inappropriate care and lose our nation's designation as the top consumer of sophisticated diagnostic imaging technology—including the highest per capita rates of magnetic resonance imaging (MRI), computed tomography (CT), and positron emission tomography (PET) exams.[65]

More common than overuse is the underuse of recommended services. Approximately 46% of patients did not receive recommended preventive or disease-specific care as defined by national guidelines. An additional 11% of care is not recommended and has potential for harm (misuse).[66]

A prominent factor of low-value care (waste) is that most physicians believe what they do is backed by solid science and that their treatment decisions reflect the latest and best research. Unfortunately, less than 20% of practice is based on solid evidence from Grade A/1 randomized, controlled trials; the rest is based on weak or no evidence or on subjective judgment. Right-sizing care requires health systems to support an HVCC to study outcomes that support quality and efficiency, while identifying and ending those that have low-value in terms of same. Only through rigorous study of the value and quality outcomes of current practice will a health system have the data required to foster change. Examples of navigation initiatives at this urban hospital that have changed practice(s) and lessened waste through use of HVCC principles are noted in Table 2. There are currently over thirty ongoing studies.

---

[65] Gregory D. Curfman, Stephen Morrissey, and Jeffrey M. Drazen, "High-Value Health Care— A Sustainable Proposition." *NEJM* 369.12 (September 19, 2013).

[66] David Nash, MD, et al., *Demand Better: Revive Our Broken Healthcare System* (Bozeman, MT: Second River Healthcare Press, 2011), 1–30.

Table 2: Summary Patient Navigation Program

SECTION	SUMMARY
Chronic Disease Management	Navigators assign and monitor video health education and work with patients and families to set short term goals. Can provide home visits and accompany patients to care locations. Navigators facilitate support groups and work with nurse educators in oncology, cardiology, rheumatology, and nephrology to assure compliance with complex care plans.
Follow-up Primary Care Appointments	Navigators are stationed in emergency room fast-track areas to provide directions and schedule appointments for primary care visits.
Reward Points	Patients and families earn points for setting and meeting self-identified goals, complying with care plans, attending support groups, and completing surveys. Points become gift cards.
Vendor Discounts	60+ vendors local to JCMC campus participate by providing discounted services to patients enrolled in navigation. Services are health related: e.g., salads vs. fries (10% discount off entrée) and no enrollment fee at fitness centers.
Employee Wellness	Walking clubs, Zumba, weight loss challenges, and semiannual employee in-house health fairs. Employees who participate in the program also have access to reward points and vendor discounts.
Partnership with local Supermarket	Patients have access to disease-specific food tours and receive coupons for fruit and vegetable purchasing at reduced cost.

The end of "business as usual" for subspecialists (cardiologist, etc.) is clearly on the horizon and many would argue has already begun. They simply must adopt organizational standards and produce quality and efficiency outcomes. Otherwise, they will not be considered "tier one" and will find themselves looking from the outside- in. Again, providers need to act as financial stewards and understand that the capricious use of subspecialists often represents an abrogation of their duties and clearly contributes to costs spiraling out of control. "Greater use of primary care has been associated with lower cost, higher patient satisfaction, fewer hospitalizations and emergency department visits, and lower mortality."[67]

---

[67] Christopher T. Koller, MPPM, et al., "Primary Care Spending Rate—A Lever for Encouraging Investment in Primary Care," *NEJM* 337.18 (November 2, 2017).

Evidence-Based Practice

To address the continued low use of evidence-based practice in medicine, a redesign in both graduate and undergraduate medical education was implemented. In collaboration with St. George's University, an offshore academic medical program, JCMC developed a four-week healthcare leadership and innovation rotation for fourth-year medical students—formed to inculcate an innovative mindset in our future physicians. In the rotation, these medical students are provided with an enhanced multidisciplinary experience in which they receive exposure and partake in high-value care projects, while also participating in leadership meetings at all levels of a large healthcare system. At the completion of the rotation, students have documented competencies in:

1. Demonstrating awareness of the changing healthcare landscape;
2. Understanding barriers to care as a result of social determinants of health; and
3. Leading a HVCC project with measurable outcomes by utilizing Lean Six Sigma tools, such as DMAIC (the acronym for define, measure, analyze, improve, and control).

This program also allows JCMC to effectively implement core Entrustable Professional Activities (EPA).[68,69] These EPAs have been developed by the Association of American Medical Colleges (AAMC) and Accreditation Council for Graduate Medical Education (ACGME) to provide guidance for medical education and better prepare students to thrive in residency programs and careers. With the

---

[68] C. El-Haddad, A. Damodaran, H. P. Mcneil, and W. Hu, "The ABCs of Entrustable Professional Activities: An Overview of 'Entrustable Professional Activities' in Medical Education," *Internal Medicine Journal* 46.9 (September 19, 2015).

[69] Kimberly Lomis, Jonathan M. Amiel, Michael S. Ryan, Karin Esposito, Michael Green, Alex Stagnaro-Green, Janet Bull, and George C. Mejicano, "Implementing an Entrustable Professional Activities Framework in Undergraduate Medical Education," *Academic Medicine* 92.6 (2017): 765–70.

success of the rotation, the program was modified and adapted for the fifty-one residents in the internal medicine residency program at JCMC. This involvement of students, residents, and professionals in a collaborative intelligence process allows for creativity and best practices and declares a call to arms to fix the healthcare system the next generation will inherit.

A good place to start reducing waste is to look at the list the Choosing Wisely initiative has compiled of practices that physicians should avoid (low-value care).[70] The American Board of Internal Medicine Foundation added ninety tests and treatments to the Choosing Wisely campaign's list of unnecessary or overused procedures. The list is the second to be released by the campaign, which launched in April 2012 with forty-five recommendations from nine leading medical groups. The effort was subsequently expanded to seventeen medical societies, each of which identified five tests or procedures that were common practice, but whose use should be questioned.

Altogether, the campaign now includes more than 130 avoidable tests and procedures from twenty-six medical groups. The recommendations include procedures and tests in geriatrics, ophthalmology, maternal health, and other categories.

According to Reuters, the groups did not consider costs when creating their lists. However, the recommendations could save billions of dollars annually, according to John Santa, director of Consumer Reports Health Ratings center, a campaign partner. One medical group with 300,000 patients could reduce its billings by $1 million annually if it followed recommendations to reduce unnecessary EKGs and bone-density scans, Santa noted.

Several business groups have signed on to Choosing Wisely in the hope of reducing healthcare costs. For example, the National Business Council on Health—with 7,000 employer members and the National

---

[70] http://www.choosingwisely.org/.

Business Group on Health, representing Fortune 500 companies and other large employers—are distributing the campaign's educational materials to its members.

Specific examples of low-value care taken from the Choosing Wisely campaign, including those submitted in the fields of cardiology, oncology, pulmonary medicine and orthopedics to name a few include:

1. Repeating screening ultrasonography, predominately looking for an aortic aneurysm, following a study with negative results.
2. Performing coronary angiography in patients with chronic stable angina with well-controlled symptoms or medical therapy or who lack specific high risk criteria and exercise test.
3. Performing echocardiography in asymptomatic patients with innocent sounding murmurs, most typically grade 1 to 2\6 short systolic, mid-peaking murmurs that are audible along left sternal border.
4. Performing routine periodic echocardiography in asymptomatic patients with mild aortic stenosis more frequently than every three to five years.
5. Routinely repeating echocardiography in asymptomatic patients with mild mitral regurgitation and normal left ventricular size and function.
6. Obtaining exercise stress testing and electrocardiogram for screening of low-risk asymptomatic adults
7. Performing imaging stress test (echocardiographic or nuclear) as the initial diagnostic test in patients with known or suspected coronary artery disease who are able to exercise and who have no resting electrocardiographic abnormalities that may interfere with interpretation of test results.
8. Measuring brain natriuretic peptides (BNP) in the initial evaluation of patients with typical findings of CHF.
9. New annual lipid screening for patients not receiving lipid-lowering drugs with diet therapy.

10. Using MRI rather than mammography in breast cancer screening test of choice for asymptomatic, average-risk women.
11. For previously treated breast cancer, performing follow-up complete blood counts, blood chemistry studies, tumor markers studies, chest radiography, and imaging studies for appropriate breast imaging.
12. Performing dual energy X-ray absorptiometry for women younger than sixty-five years of age in the absence of risk factors; screening low-risk individuals for hepatitis B virus infection; screening for cervical cancer and low-risk women age sixty-five or younger and in women who have had a total hysterectomy for benign disease.
13. Screening for colorectal cancer in adults older than age seventy-five with a life expectancy of less than ten years. New repeat colonoscopy within five years of the index colonoscopy in asymptomatic patients found to have low-risk adenomas.
14. Screening for prostate cancer in men older than seventy-five with life expectancy of less than ten years.
15. Using CA–125 antigen levels to screen women for ovarian cancer in the absence of increase risk.
16. Performing imaging studies in patients with nonspecific low back pain.
17. Performing preoperative chest radiography with the absence of clinical suspicion for intrathoracic pathology.

Other Examples of Institutions That Regularly Rollout Evidence-Based Recommendations for Their Clinicians

In Southern California, Kaiser Permanente's evidence-based medicine services, which has existed since the early 1990s, examine the use of new technologies and procedures for their entire health system. They employ ten evidence-oriented analysts to conduct rapid reviews, which are used to provide Kaiser's clinical practice guidelines, as well as medical technology assessments. They do about 205 to 400 evidenced-based reviews each year; about twenty pertaining to new technologies.

Cincinnati Children's Hospital Medical Center in Ohio uses a similar model to rapidly incorporate evidence into practice. The program has three full-time appraisers review the evidence, the typical rapid review taking about two to four weeks.

In 2016, the American College of Physicians (ACP) launched its Center for Evidence Reviews in order to develop in-house evidence reviews that help inform the clinical practice guidelines program in the country.

Today, there are still only a few evidence-based practice centers in the United States. We strongly urge that their time has come.

Setting Up an HVCC for a Health System

There are clearly a number of ways to approach setting up a high-value care center. The center could be used as a mean to:

- Rapidly incorporate new evidence-based protocols into practice(s);
- Focus on outcomes and patients' wishes when deciding on practice changes;
- Provide answers on best practice to physicians and other care providers;
- Note common requestors and develop policies that meet and anticipate their needs. Common requesters could include, chiefs of clinical departments, chief medical officer, clinical researchers, purchasing units, etc.; and
- Provide answers that include:
  - Summary table(s) with details on published studies,
  - Grade(s) on quality of evidence,
  - Behaviorist input on patient needs,

- ○ Economist viewpoints: ROI (return on investment), and
- ○ Best dissemination practices. (Yes, a science of implementation exists.)

A successful HVCC, see Table 3 for examples and outcomes at JCMC, should have the commitment of the health system leadership, including dedication of appropriate resources to the program. The center should have a dedicated leader who will be accountable to for program outcomes, including tracking and trending practice changes and results. A pharmacy leader and others with expertise in research,

Table 3: Examples of 2015–2016 HVCC initiatives and outcomes at Jersey City Medical Center-RWJ Barnabas Health (JCMC)

PROJECT	INTERVENTION	METRIC	RESULT
Early Mobilization and reduced sedation of ICU patients	Dedicated Physical Therapist and PharmD in ICU with protocol driven actions	LOS in ICU n= 1503 patients	2015: 10.3 days 2016: 9.5 days
Hep C case finding, referral, and treatment	Opt-out screening of all adult admits age 45–65	Number Screened and treatment	2015: 0 screened 2016: 3689 screened, 63 positive, 50 treatments completed
Right-sizing radiology for diagnosis of pulmonary embolism	Pilot of commercial software	Appropriate diagnostics TP/TN	Software failed pilot. Not purchased. Currently being studied for diagnosis of low back pathology
Alternative treatment for Barrett's Esophagus	Cryotherapy vs Radiofrequency Ablation (RFA)*	Complication rate n= 96 patients	Serious side effects: 0 (1%*) Strictures: 0 (3%*) Repeat required within 2 years: 1 (vs 1/3 of pts receiving RFA)
Palliative care as goal setting with family and patient	Early consultation with goal setting	Average admission to consult (days) Conversion to hospice care during inpatient admission Q12016 n=81 Q12017 n=88	Q12016: 7.8 days Q12017: 5.2 days Q12016: conversion rate 29% Q12017 conversion rate: 39%

analysis, and change dynamics will also be needed. A core mission for the program will always be education.

Antibiotics: An Example of an HVCC Initiative

Tremendous how a true antimicrobial stewardship program seems to have resonated across the country. It's hard to imagine a hospital system in the country today without some effort in this regard. Certainly, the issue of antimicrobial resistance is a huge one, owing to the overuse of antibiotics today. There are certainly many reasons for this, but in the outpatient setting, patients expect to get an antibiotic prescription even if the illness is viral in nature and an antibiotic is not indicated. Many physicians simply refuse to continue to argue with patients. Note that the COVID-19 pandemic has heightened the anxiety for patients, with physicians fielding passionate requests for unproven antivirals and antibiotics. This mismatch between patient expectations, even in the Oval Office, and science tells us that this issue is one that needs continued vigilance and innovation.

One of the areas of particular interest to me in the hospital setting was use of intravenous antibiotics for far longer than they were required, thereby exposing the patient to complications and prolonging the hospital stay. There is no magic or evidence-based literature that directs seven or ten days of intravenous antibiotic usage. The literature, in fact, is clear that such antibiotic use should *not* be employed for more than twenty-four or forty-eight hours after the patient has clinically improved. The epidemic of hospital-centered Clostridium difficile (C diff.) diarrheal infections can be attributed to antibiotic use and has become a huge problem, leading to many hospitalizations that were avoidable.

HVCC initiatives centering on respiratory illness leading to the overprescribing of antibiotics at our hospital promulgated these statements for our physicians:

High-Value Care advice 1: Clinicians should not perform testing or initiate antibiotic therapy in patients with bronchitis unless pneumonia is suspected.

High-Value Care advice 2: Clinicians should test patients with symptoms suggestive of group A streptococcal pharyngitis (for example, persistent fevers, anterior cervical adenitis, and tonsillopharyngeal exudates, or other appropriate combination of symptoms) by rapid antigen detection test and/or culture for group A streptococcus. Clinicians should treat patients with antibiotics only if they have confirmed streptococcal pharyngitis.

High-Value Care advice 3: Clinicians should reserve antibiotic treatment for acute rhinosinusitis for patients with persistent symptoms for more than ten days; onset of severe symptoms or signs of high fever (>39°C); and purulent nasal discharge, or facial pain lasting for at least three consecutive days, or the onset of worsening symptoms following a typical viral illness that lasted five days and was initially improving (double sickening).

High-Value Care advice 4: Clinicians should not prescribe antibiotics for patients with the common cold.

Why should an HVCC address this issue? Acute respiratory tract infection (ARTI)—which includes acute uncomplicated bronchitis, pharyngitis, rhinosinusitis, and the common cold—is the most common reason for outpatient physician office sick visits and antibiotic prescription in adults. Antibiotics are prescribed at more than 100 million adult ambulatory care visits annually, and 41% of these prescriptions are for respiratory conditions.[71] Inappropriate antibiotic use for ARTI is an important contributor to antibiotic resistance, an urgent public health threat. In the United States, at least 2 million antibiotic-resistant illnesses and 23,000 deaths occur each year, costing

---

[71] Aaron M. Harris, MD, MPH, et al., "Appropriate Antibiotic Use for Acute Respiratory Tract Infection in Adults: Advice from High-Value Care from American College of Physicians and Center for Disease Control and Prevention," *Annals of Internal Medicine* 164 (March 15, 2016).

to the U.S. economy at least $30 billion. Increased community use of antibiotics is highly correlated with emerging antibiotic-resistant infections. In places with greater prescribing of broad-spectrum anti-biotics, specifically extended-spectrum cephalosporin's and macrolides, rates of multidrug-resistant pneumococcal disease are higher.[72]

Antibiotics are also responsible for the largest number of medication-related adverse events, implicated in one of every five visits to emergency departments for adverse drug reactions. Adverse events range in severity from mild (for example, diarrhea and rash) to life-threatening (for example, Stevens-Johnson syndrome, anaphy-laxis, or sudden cardiac death). Although data on adverse events after inappropriate antibiotic use are not available, an estimated 5% to 25% of patients who use antibiotics have adverse events, and about one in 1,000 have a serious adverse event. Clostridium difficile diarrhea, men-tioned earlier, causes nearly 500,000 infections and 29,300 deaths in the United States each year, leading to an estimated $1 billion in extra medical costs.[73]

Other HVCC-worthy examples follow and include the use of the Physician's Orders for Life-Sustaining Treatment (POLST) document to provide concrete instructions and substance to a severe illness or end-of-life care program and an imaging stewardship effort to right-size the use of CT scans and MRIs. HVCCs can also address correct use of rheumatologic markers, transfusion needs, and appropriate admission to observation units to decrease hospitalization exposure and cost.

POLST

POLST (the acronym for Physician Orders for Life-Sustaining Treat-ment) is a set of medical orders that help give seriously ill or frail elderly

---

[72] Ibid.
[73] Ibid.

patients more control over their end-of-life care. Produced on a distinctive green form and signed by both the doctor or advanced practice nurse *and* the patient/surrogate, POLST specifies the types of medical treatment that a patient wishes to receive toward the end of life or through a serious illness. As a result, POLST can prevent unwanted or medically ineffective treatment, reduce patient and family suffering, and help ensure that patients' wishes are honored. Documentation on the POLST form includes:

- Goals of care for the patient;
- Preferences regarding cardiopulmonary resuscitation attempts;
- Preferences regarding use of intubation and mechanical ventilation for respiratory failure;
- Preference for artificially administered nutrition and hydration; and
- Other specific preferences regarding medical interventions that are desired or declined.

The HVCC initiative included quarterly poster presentations to staff, in service to nursing and social worker employees of the subacute and long-term care facilities (community partners not owned by system), and a commitment for POLST sheets to be transferred with the patient from those facilities for any ER visit.

Imaging Stewardship

Like antibiotic stewardship, imaging stewardship attempts to right-size diagnostic X-rays, MRIs, and CT scans so valuable diagnosis information is not lost, while ensuring that the patient does not receive unnecessary radiation doses or unnecessary expense. Making necessary investments and publicly committing to a cultural shift toward appropriateness—and away from easy access to imaging—is a critical part of bringing value to a healthcare organization and its patients. To accomplish this, the HVCC initiative assured that leadership would:

- Appoint a single leader within each imaging specialty, and establish joint accountability among the multiple relevant specialties.
- Make imaging specialists responsible for executing appropriateness interventions.
- Implement interventions to ensure systematic evaluation of appropriateness at the time of ordering and encourage dialogue between referring physicians and imaging experts.
- Monitor imaging utilization and appropriateness scores for providers and trace per-capita costs and radiation doses.
- Inform referring physicians about their imaging utilization rates and the best available measures of imaging appropriateness.
- Identify key knowledge gaps on imaging appropriateness and educate referring physicians on relevant evidence-based guidelines.[74]

Rheumatologic Markers

One of the best opportunities to make efficient use of an HVCC is in the field of rheumatology. It has become quite apparent in literature that the use of rheumatologic serologies has become a haphazard, shotgun-like process that wastes money, incorrectly diagnoses patients, and contributes to wasteful care. A good case in point would be the use of the antinuclear antibody (ANA), which is, generally, only believed by many practitioners to indicate a diagnosis of SLE (lupus). However, it can also be seen in rheumatoid arthritis, and, in fact, the number of true lupus patients in United States was approximately 100,000, while the number of rheumatoid arthritic patients was close to 5 million.

---

[74]Tom Sullivan, "Apple, IBM, Google Hold Keys to Make EHR Data Actionable," *Healthcare IT News* (September 2017).

So contrary to what many clinicians believe, if you suffer from an inflammatory arthritic condition, the likelihood of you having rheumatoid arthritis, rather than SLE, is roughly 50 to 1. Therefore, most cases will turn out to be rheumatoid arthritis. Interesting, no?

Currently, there is no widely accepted clinical application with embedded hard stops that can caution physicians about ordering rheumatologic tests when the American College of Rheumatology (ACR) guidelines are not met for a suspected diagnosis. Many physicians are unaware of the proper indications, sensitivity, specificity, prevalence, pre-test probability, costs, and clinical utility when ordering rheumatologic test. Prevalence plays a key role when considering rheumatologic testing because testing at rheum clinic vs. a primary care provider's office will yield different results, with the latter, more often than not, having lower positive predictive value. Studies show that there is a significant amount of waste when ordering rheumatologic test in a primary care setting because these tests are ordered well before there is a referral to rheumatology.[75] The overuse of common serum rheumatologic tests, such as antinuclear antibody (ANA) and rheumatoid factor (RF), lead to unnecessary laboratory workups and referrals, which ultimately leads to increased hospital costs. The HVCC initiative widely disseminated the ACR guidelines (including a multidisciplinary grand rounds) and appointed a rheumatologist to be available for staff and laboratory queries and interpretations of results.

Transfusion Stewardship

The issue of transfusion of red blood cells, platelets, and coagulation factors represents another area of significant waste in medicine. While attending the tenth anniversary of the Jersey City Medical Center's

---

[75] Adapted by Marian Valentin, MD, *Arthritis Care & Research* 65.3 (March 2013). American College of Rheumatology, accessed August 2, 2014, www.rheumatology.org.

Level Two Trauma Program, I happened to notice a station in the back of the auditorium manned by a salesperson for the thromboelastography (TEG) hemostasis analyzer system. It offered, for the first time, the ability to exactly quantitate how much of each clotting factor is required during trauma, surgery, and major bleeds. Additionally, the platelet-mapping function would advise the clinician as to whether the medicines directed at inhibiting platelet function were succeeding or needed to be redosed, and that information could help decide when it would be safe to operate. Historically, replacing clotting factors has been a guessing game, while the transfusion of red blood cells has held onto an age-old rule of thumb: to maintain one's hemoglobin and hematocrit at a minimum of 10/30. This "fact" had no basis in evidence-based literature, and, in many cases and much to our chagrin, it could lead to more harm than good.

The HVCC initiative fostered the purchase of the TEG and trauma and general surgeons began to reassess effective and efficient use of blood products. This is a new initiative with ROI forecasted but not yet calculated as to the volume of products used and the shortening of operating room waits.

Observation Units

A number of years ago, the Centers for Medicare and Medicaid Services (CMS) mandated that all hospitals initiate an observation unit, either geographically located or virtual, in order to cut down on long stay hospitalizations by treating those cases that required only up to forty-eight hours before discharge. To offer a historical perspective, many of these "observation" patients would have spent five to seven days, on average, in the hospital. In reality, they never required such lengthy hospitalizations, producing a colossal waste of resources. In fact, the observation designation is considered an outpatient designation and is strictly overseen. My units over the years have averaged between 3,500 to 5,000 patients per year with few untoward outcomes, spending on average eighteen to twenty hours in the unit before discharge.

Patients under observation (not in-patient) are often unclear about their status and have a very short period of time for education to ensure appropriate ambulatory follow-up. Those patients with chronic disease enrolled in the Wealth from Health program, who needed to be seen in the observation unit, did demonstrably better than nonmembers as measured by return to the ER and compliance with first outpatient visit. HVCC recognized this important touchpoint for the community and enrollment efforts increased membership in program.

Finally, redesigning both graduate and postgraduate medical education through the framework of a High-Value Care Center provided a new generation of physicians with the right tools required to assess, test, and improve delivery of care.

CHAPTER EIGHT

PRECISION MEDICINE, A CAUTIONARY NOTE

L et's embrace the era of precision medicine, but understand that its true value lies in adopting the panoramic view of the individual—that is, adding the physiomics, anatomics, proteomics, metabolomics, microbiomics, and exomics to the current discussion of genomics, epigenomics, and transcriptomics.

Physiomics refers to one's physiologic metrics such as heart rate and blood pressure. *Anatomics* is our individual anatomy. The *genome* refers to the 6 billion letters that make up one's DNA sequence. Likewise, the *proteomics* (all of your proteins), the *metabolomics* (your metabolites), the *microbiomics* (representing the microbes that inhabit you), and the *epigenome* (chemical compounds that modify the expression and function of the genome) comprise the side chains of DNA and how it is packaged. Finally, there's the *exome*, which is the environment you are exposed to. Lastly, for people to do anything with their DNA, it must be transcribed to RNA, hence the *transcriptome*. One of the exciting things about precision medicine is finally being able to address the "unexplained drug resistance, genomic heterogeneity of tumors, insufficient means for monitoring responses and tumor recurrence, and limited knowledge about the use of drug combinations" in the field of precision oncology.[76]

---

[76] Victor Dzau, MD, et al., "Realizing the Full Potential of Precision Medicine in Health and Healthcare," *JAMA* 316.16 (October 25, 2016).

Rachel Naomi Remen, MD once wrote, "Facts bring us to knowledge; stories bring us to wisdom."[77] With these new facts, the stories will be better informed.

Additionally, "Opportunities to identify persons with rare loss of function mutations that protect against common diseases may point to attractive drug targets for broad patient populations."[78] An example of why the family history is still relevant in the genomics era is that "given the germline mutations which account for 5 to 10% of cases of breast cancer in the U.S. and that women who develop cancer associated with such mutations at a relatively young age, account for a disproportionate share of life-years lost due to cancer." These women can be identified and referred for genetic testing.[79]

"With these new metrics, it must still be remembered that our health is affected by our physical and social environments, our genes, our economic and educational opportunities, and too much lesser degree, medical care we receive."[80]

According to the healthcare consulting firm, The Studer Group, patient treatment hospitals (disease and cure specific) are becoming the rule rather than the exception.[81] However, precision medicine will undoubtedly bring about an age of diagnostic and prognostic uncertainty, not at all what the word "precision" implies. "Defined as treatments targeted to the needs of individual patients on the basis of genetic, biomarker, phenotypic, or psychosocial characteristics that distinguish the patient from other patients with similar clinical presentations. All is rather straightforward, that is to say, to improve clinical outcomes and

---

[77] Rachel Naomi Remen, *Kitchen Table Wisdom: Stories That Heal*, (New York: Riverhead Books, 1997).

[78] Francis Collins, MD, PhD, et al., "A New Initiative in Precision Medicine," *NEJM* 372 (February 26, 2015).

[79] M. Doerr, et al., "Family History Still Relevant in the Genomic Era," *Cleveland Clinic Journal of Medicine* 79.5 (May 2012).

[80] S.A. Schroeder, "We Can Do Better—Improving the Health of the American People," *NEJM* 357 (September 20, 2007).

[81] Quint Studer, *Hardwiring Excellence* (Gulf Breeze, FL: Fire Starter Publishing, 2003), 2–44.

minimize unnecessary side effects."[82] However, "(a)ssessing and acting on these probabilities will require approaches to data presentation and risk quantification of uncertainty for which we are largely ill-equipped and that we already struggle with."[83]

For genomic-based interventions to gather support and continued funding they must show convincing evidence of value. Accurate and reliable genetic tests are crucial, but their clinical usefulness must demonstrate greater value than existing interventions. In fact, "a number of persuasive genomic associations with disease risk, excepting rare Mendelian conditions, remain small."[84]

Pharmacogenomics, the study of genomic influence on drug metabolism, has now become important in a practical use of genomics. (e.g., a drug and gene interaction).[85]

"Misinterpretation of genomic data, even by medical professionals," is well documented, resulting in a wide range of harm to patients. Incomplete information does not inform good decision making. To be clear, the field is exciting, but let's walk before we run ... The impending marriage between precision medicine and population health will need to utilize technology (i.e., apps and mobile devices) to gather the necessary data that will drive results, traveling seamlessly outside the walls of the hospital.[86]

Moving genomic and other molecular information into routine healthcare delivery is critical to a precision-medicine powered health system. Improving workforce education, training, and clinical decision support to understand when and how to use genomic technologies is also critical. Interestingly enough, some of the most important benefits

[82] J. Larry Jameson, M.D., Ph.D. and Dan L. Longo, M.D., "Precision medicine-personalized, problematic, and promising," *NEJM* 372 (June 4, 2015).

[83] David Hunter, MB, B.S., ScD, "Uncertainty in the Era of Precision Medicine," *NEJM* 375.8 (August 25, 2016).

[84] Christopher Chute, MD, DrPH, et al., "Genomic Medicine, Health Information Technology, and Patient Care," *JAMA* 309.14 (April 10, 2013).

[85] Amy McGuire, JD, PhD, et al., "The Indispensable Role of Professional Judgment Genomic Medicine," *JAMA* 309.14 (April 10, 2013).

[86] Christopher Chute, MD, DrPH, et al., "Genomic Medicine, Health Information Technology, and Patient Care," *JAMA* 309.14 (April 10, 2013).

of precision medicine may involve identifying healthy individuals at elevated risk of disease, allowing for the targeting of effective preventive therapies. Although there is increasing pressure to engage consumers, researchers and clinicians have little experience in thinking of the participants as partners who will be actively engaged throughout the research process.[87] This must change now and will require a major attitudinal adjustment, to say the least, between providers and patients alike.

It also will demand a greater tolerance of uncertainty and a greater facility for calculating and interpreting probabilities. New tools to extract information from cancer genomes that include the mutations that occur somatically, cancer genome sequencing, and the functional changes that result from both these mutations—along with epigenetic events, gene-expression alterations, and tumors will be needed. We will need to help our patients absorb large amounts of information,[88] not to mention, educating the physicians.

Though oncologists today are clearly using genomic data when treating lung cancer and melanoma, the responses are quite varied. Unfortunately, this is the case with some patients whose test results would indicate that they are likely responders. This suggests that additional genes may be involved in mediating a patient's response to a particular drug. Large data sets of patients will be needed to shed light on this issue.[89]

Examples of Conditions in Which Precision Medicine Has Been Used

- BCR-ABL: Imatinib
- Chronic myeloid leukemia

---

[87] Jeremy Bey, PhD, et al., "Training the Workforce for 21st Century Science," *JAMA* 316.16 (October 25, 2016).

[88] Steven Lipstein, MHA, et al., "Workforce for 21st Century Health and Healthcare," *JAMA* 316.16 (October 25, 2016).

[89] Bridget M. Kuehn, MSJ, "Alliance Aims for Standardized, Shareable Genomic Data," *JAMA* 310.3 (July 17, 2013).

- Coronary artery disease
- Cystic fibrosis
- Factor V Leiden: Avoid prothrombotics
- G551D: Ivacaftor
- Hepatitis C
- HIV/AIDS
- Kidney transplant rejection
- Lung cancer
- Thrombosis

Dr. Collins, et al. go as far as to suggest building a "cancer knowledge network" to keep all the molecular and medical data in digital form so that they can educate all healthcare workers, scientists, and, most importantly, patients on a level that they can understand.[90] In fact, President Obama's call for 1 million participants in the Precision Medicine Initiative would have been an amazing step forward.

---

[90] Francis Collins, MD, PhD, et al., "A New Initiative in Precision Medicine," *NEJM* 372 (February 26, 2015).

CHAPTER NINE

PERSONALIZED HEALTHCARE

E very profession has its guru, its pithy spokesperson whose words antedated or predicted events to come in a most prescient way. For medical professionals, it was Dr. William Osler, a Canadian physician born in 1849 who helped found Johns Hopkins University and is most noted for bringing medical education out of the classroom and into the wards and bedsides of patients. Osler often stated, "It is much more important to know what sort of patient has a disease than what sort of disease a patient has." So true then, and so amazingly accurate today.

This reminds me of a funny story. A number of years ago, I worked alongside a rather accomplished rheumatologist and extremely funny man, Dr. Robert Lahita. Bob was indeed a student of the history of medicine and maintained on a prominent wall in the common area in our suite of offices, nine black-and-white framed photos of the giants in medicine: Osler, Fleming, and so on. Great physicians for sure, but they gave me the creeps after a while, staring at their frowning faces every day. So one day, I removed four of them and hung a large color photo of my wife and me hiking Mt. Rainier in Seattle, (a favorite of mine) in their place. Well, the next day I put the key in my door and entered my office to be greeted by a string of four-letter words uttered by a flapping fish mounted on a board. Additionally, I noted all of my diplomas turned upside down or simply reversed. I couldn't stop laughing, and yes, my picture stayed put. Now to continue…

Approaching each patient as an individual has eroded over the years due to increasingly truncated visit times, mandatory electronic medical record (EMR) charting, the insistence on technological involvement in most cases, even if not always indicated, and especially in many safety-net urban areas with linguistic and cultural differences. Witnessing this firsthand has been difficult to accept as the very underpinnings of why a medical student should pick internal medicine or another primary care discipline as their chosen field has been greatly damaged by putting a machine between patient and doctor. The time spent with patients has morphed into a minute-by-minute schedule of events, which is complicated by the cumbersome federal EMR charting mandate. Many practices have hired scribes solely for this purpose, adding significantly to their overhead—or even worse for the majority of those not willing to add the expense, leaving Sundays to come in to do the charting that went amiss during the week. Essentially, working seven days a week, which leads to burnout of untold proportion. Physicians are retiring early, quitting, or becoming embittered, affecting their personal lives immeasurably. This is no exaggeration.

On the other hand, as discussed earlier, genomics, proteomics, pharmacogenomics, etc. have risen in importance and emphasis. In fact, this field of precision medicine will ultimately lead to new diagnostics and therapeutics no doubt. Technology will be a critical retainer of data that must be managed.

Roy Ziegelstein, undoubtedly an Osler devotee, used the word "personomics"—understanding the unique circumstances of the patient—in his article, stating "that such an understanding can only be developed when the relevant psychological, social, cultural, behavioral, and economic factors are obtained."[91] Personomics determines how disease reveals itself phenotypically (outwardly) and how an individual with a disease responds to treatment. For example, a child with severe asthma living in a home with smokers only uses an inhaler at certain

---

[91] Roy Ziegelstein, MD, MACP, "Personomics," *JAMA* 175 (June 1, 2015).

times of the month (if at all, when there is money to pay for it) and uses it improperly because of improper oversight, and so forth. Not that uncommon and an easy example of how personomics changes his disease outcome.

Therefore, clinicians should place a higher premium on fully involving patients in their own healthcare to the extent the patients choose. They should employ high-quality, reliable tools and skills for shared decision making with patients and tailored to clinical needs, patient goals, social circumstances, and the patients' preferred degree of control. They or their proxies need to ferret out these details as painstakingly as other parts of the history and physical.

Our country needs healthcare that learns by avoiding past mistakes and adopts newfound successes. This preoccupation with repeating something over and over again until it works is *not* going to happen. What was Einstein's observations on this phenomenon? Pick one, here are three:

- "We cannot solve our problems with the same thinking we used when we created them."
- "Imagination is more important than knowledge."
- "Insanity: doing the same thing over and over again and expecting different results."

Furthermore, to double down, we do not need a new generation of leaders who simply rush to copy their mentors' efforts, unless those mentors are dedicated to creating an "an army of innovators" or a core of "change agents." Dr. Krumholz and his colleagues put it well: "a learning health system."[92] Also, the only acceptable measures of success need to be the ones that are important, understandable, and actionable for patients. For example, the patient activating measure (PAM) describes

---

[92] Harlan Krumholz, MD, SD, et al., "Data Acquisition, Curation and Use for a Continuously Learning Health System." *JAMA* 316.16 (October 25, 2016).

when patients are moved to actively self-manage their chronic diseases.[93] There is a big difference between knowing what to do and doing it! So many times I witness a healthcare professional checking off their long list of responsibilities that we have become convinced are imperative, either because those items are reimbursable or because some healthcare expert deems it the fad of the day. Did my patients much care about all my work to help them if they didn't feel better or were not able to engage in those activities that brought them joy? Could you blame them?

Personomics and the Wholesale Club

Wikipedia describes wholesale club or otherwise known as warehouse club as a "retail store, usually selling a wide variety of merchandise, in which customers purchase large, wholesale quantities of the store's products, which makes these clubs attractive to both bargain hunters and small business owners." The clubs are able to keep prices low due to their no-frills format. In addition, customers may be required to pay annual membership fees in order to shop there. This concept is similar to the consumer's cooperative supermarkets found in Europe, although the stores are bigger and not cooperatively owned. Maybe the time has arrived to use this concept in healthcare.

This is how it might look based on suggestions made by the Precision Medicine Initiative which is a long-term project that involves the National Institutes of Health (NIH)[94] and multiple other research centers, aiming to comprehend how a person's genetics, environment, and lifestyle can contribute to the optimum approach of preventing or treating disease. Their program is to involve a cohort of 1 million people

---

[93] Judith Hibbard, et al., "Development of the Patient Activation Measure (PAM): Conceptualizing and Measuring Activation in Patients and Consumers," *HSR Health Services* Research (August 2004).

[94] "What is the Precision Medicine Initiative?" *NIH U.S. National Library of Medicine* (January 9, 2018).

from around the country who will provide data, biological samples, and additional information about their health. Researchers will utilize the data to study a long list of disease entities to better predict disease risk, understand just how disease occurs, and find improved diagnosis and treatment.

Some of the scientific opportunities revolve around the following:

- **Developing quantitative estimates of risk** for a range of diseases by integrating environmental exposures, genetic factors, and gene-environment interactions. We expect new and unexpected associations.
- **Identifying the determinants of safety and efficacy for commonly used therapeutics.** Facts: There are 4 billion prescriptions filled each year by retail pharmacies; 49% of American adults take at least one medication, and 22% take three or more. There is a wide variation in response and 4.5 million ambulatory visits occur each year, and thousands of hospitalizations due to adverse reactions to medications. The opportunity will exist to comprehensively identify predictors of individual response to therapy.[95]
- **Discovering biomarkers that identify individuals with an increased risk of developing common diseases.** We will be able to develop causal relationships between specific metabolites and disease pathogenesis (cause). Then we can identify opportunities for disease prevention and/or early therapeutic intervention.
- **Using home and mobile health (mHealth) technologies to correlate body measurements and environmental exposures with health outcomes.** Thus we can measure ambulatory blood pressures, physiologic signs of mental health, GPS monitoring and environmental exposures, nutrition, physical exercise, sleep behavior, social

---

[95] Harlan Krumholz, MD, SD, et al., "Data Acquisition, Curation and Use for a Continuously Learning Health System." *JAMA* 316.16 (October 25, 2016).

interactions, and sensor-detected atrial fibrillation episodes, putting people at risk for embolic stroke, to name a few.

- **Determining the clinical impact of loss-of-function mutations.** These cause specific genetic diseases and with a large cohort of patients in total will offer possible determinants of health and disease in order to offer therapy in the future. Thus whether a heterozygous state for these mutations predisposes an individual to Alzheimer's disease or whether a loss-of-function mutation(s) in those with very low levels of LDL cholesterol and whose cardiovascular risk is quite low also can offer desirable effects on health.

- **Developing new disease classifications and relationships.** This large and complex set of data points will allow for the opportunity to discover unexpected connections and new subtypes of disease as recently seen in some cancers, autism, and heart disease.

- **Empowering participants with data to improve their own health.** Patients will have access to their own data and real-time sensor information so that they can take pre-emptive action when so alerted.

- **Enrolling PMI cohort participants in clinical trials of targeted therapies.** Tremendous opportunity for clinical trials here that will expedite greatly more targeted interventions. Dr. Armstrong, et al from the Department of Medicine at Massachusetts General and the Department of Stem Cell Regenerative Biology Harvard University established in fact a "pathway service" dedicated to training residents patient-based scientific inquiry. "In contrast to consultation services that focus on diagnostic and therapeutic recommendations, this pathway service aims to shine a spotlight on that we do not know ... and refer patients if they have an extreme or unusual phenotype that no one is able to explain adequately."[96]

---

[96] Katrina Armstrong, MD, et al., "Toward a Culture of Scientific Inquiry—The Role of Medical Teaching Services," *NEJM* 378.1 (January 4, 2018).

It is crucially important to note that people who historically have been underrepresented in biomedical research will be represented in sufficient numbers to learn a great deal about all peoples in this country. Health disparities defined as significant differences in health between populations that are more or less socially advantaged or disadvantaged, persists across the United States—hence the differential disease prevalence, unequal access to treatment, and variable response to therapy. For example, Pacific Islanders are unable to convert the antiplatelet drug clopidogrel into its active form and face greater risk for adverse outcomes following angioplasty.[97] African-Americans comprise 12% of the nation's population, but only 5% of clinical trial participants.[98] Many diseases of the respiratory system are either linked causally or exacerbated by environmental exposures that disproportionately affect disadvantaged populations.

What is important to understand is that the information and data to be gleaned from this setup is exactly what is missing from the healthcare system today. By arranging for these particulars to be part of one's extremely comprehensive database, we would finally possess the type of patient data that will give us answers long sought and the promise of pushing our health understanding light years ahead. Shouldn't we as a society push to help this cohort get off the ground as such thinking provides real hope in revamping our system?[99]

This new system specifically will compile:

1. Individual demographics and contact information: date and place of birth, sex and gender, detailed the multiple races\ethnicities, name, mailing address, phone number, cell phone number, email address, marital status, educational status, and occupation/income.

[97] AM Bhopalwala, RA Hong, et al., "Routine screening for CYP2C19 polymorphisms for patients being treated with clopidogrel is not recommended," *Hawaiian Journal of Medicine and Public Health* (January 2015). https://www.ncbi.nlm.nih.gov/pubmed/25628978.

[98] U.S. Food and Drug Administration, "Clinical Trials Shed Light on Minority Health" (updated January 20, 2018). https://www.fda.gov/ForConsumers/ConsumerUpdates/ucm349063.htm.

[99] Harlan Krumholz, MD, SD, et al., "Data Acquisition, Curation and Use for a Continuously Learning Health System." *JAMA* 316.16 (October 25, 2016).

2. Terms of consent and personal preferences for participation in the project: fine-grained consent for options to participate: e.g., received research results.
3. Self-reported measures: pain skills, disease-specific symptoms, functional capabilities, quality of life and well-being, gender identity, and structured family health history.
4. Behavioral and lifestyle measures: diet, physical activity, alternative therapies, smoking, and alcohol assessment of known risk factors (e.g., guns, illicit drug use).
5. Sensor-based observations through phones, wearables, home-based devices: location, activity monitors, cardiac rate and rhythm monitoring, and respiratory rate. Wearable sensors include:
   - Abbott Diabetes Care
   - ADAAM (Asthma monitoring)
   - Google Smart Contact lenses
   - HealthPatchMD
   - Helius by Proteus Digital Health
   - I Sono Health
   - Leaf Healthcare Ulcer Sensor
   - Smart Stop by Chrono Therapeutics
   - Valedo Back Therapy
   - Vitaliti by Cloud Dx
6. Structured clinical data derived from EMRs, diagnosis and billing codes (ICD\CPT), clinical lab values, medications, and problem lists.
7. Unstructured and specialized types of clinical data derived from the EMRs: narrative documents, images, and EKG and EEG waveform data.
8. Baseline health exam: vital signs, medication assessment, and past medical history.
9. Healthcare claims data: periods of coverage, charges, and associative billing codes are received by public and private payers, such

as outpatient pharmacy dispensing such as the product, dose, and amount.

10. Research specific observation: research questionnaires, ecological momentary assessments, disease specific monitors (such as glucometers and spirometers), and performance measures (such as six-minute walk test).

11. Bio specimens-derived lab data: genomics, metabolites, cell-free DNA, single-cell studies, infectious exposures, standard clinical chemistries, and histopathology.

12. Geospatial and environmental data: weather, air quality, environmental pollutant levels, food deserts, walk ability, population density, and climate change.

13. Other data: social networking, such as Twitter feeds, social context from cell phone text and voice, and over-the-counter medication purchases.

Moreover, design that allows participants to be re-contacted for further study based on individual findings provides an invaluable opportunity to understand biological mechanisms that link biomarkers to traits and individuals. How this information remains secure and confidential will need to be addressed and solved before the initiative moves forward.

CHAPTER TEN

REMOTE MONITORING AND THE TRANSFORMATION OF THE PRACTICE OF MEDICINE

The emerging standard for accessibility will provide seamless care and extends beyond physical access to care. There will never be enough primary care physicians to service the American population in my lifetime. In fact, I do not believe it even necessary because the burgeoning number of allied healthcare professionals (nurse practitioners, physician assistants, certified nurse midwives, etc.) can handle the more routine cases, which allows the complex cases to be addressed by the physicians. But accessing your physician's office via email, mobile apps, Skype, and community health kiosks are just some of the ways to connect in this new world. Physicians must be compensated, however, for such virtual visits, maybe in the form of a monthly fee for that type of access versus the antiquated fee-for-service model.

Perhaps an occasional visit to a brick-and-and mortar establishment (just enough to maintain that human touch, literally), but in any fully capitated environment, a perfect match. Frankly, when I practice primary care medicine, I am acutely aware that probably more than half of the patients did *not* have to see me in the office that day. Patients will need to become comfortable with this hybrid approach, by which virtual medicine meets traditional medicine.

My experience with remote monitoring dates back at least fifteen or so years, when armed with a grant of $25,000, I purchased four computers outfitted with a stethoscope, weight scale, pulse oximetry, and temperature probe. Four of my private patients volunteered to let my residents bring one of the computers into their homes (back then computers then were heavy and quite large) and arrange for a remote monitoring visit with me back at the office. The residents would place the stethoscope on the patient's chest and lungs, while heart sounds and breath sounds were coming over the computer. The heart sounds were easy to hear clearly, but as far as the clarity of the lung sounds, everyone sounded like they were in congestive heart failure. Not ready for prime time.

Subsequently, I arranged for the purchase of twenty-five remote-monitoring units (much smaller and more accurate) to be placed in the home-care business of the hospital that I worked in at that time. They were so successful that the home-care agency was able to monitor the patients more accurately and cost effectively. We did, however, experience an anxious moment in the beginning when a patient's son stepped on the scale (despite being told not to do so) with his weight registering at the home-care agency, not his mother's weight. Needless to say, all kinds of bells and whistles went off before we were able to ascertain that an error had occurred.

The smartphones we discuss in this book represent a far cry from what will be true in the near future:

- The number of inputs to the smartphone will be staggering, whether DNA samplings, breath analyses, blood samples, and so many more.
- The tenets of precision medicine and population health will come together in a most unique way utilizing such a smart phone.
- Virtual visits will become a routine phenomenon, hopefully becoming a runaway success for both patient and provider alike.

"Hundreds of vendors offer telehealth products or peripherals that range from simple videoconferencing software to hospital unit—wide monitoring systems, all turnkey solutions to bundle hardware, software, and implementation support. For instance, some technologies are more commonly used for episodic disease treatment, either in an acute or ambulatory setting. Others are better suited for disease prevention or management and are more often deployed in clinics or patient homes."[100] Much will depend on what you decide the clinical uses will be, how intense you need to monitor a particular patient, and what type of the business relationship you have with your vendors and the subsequent cost.

Let's explore further. The Advisory Board, an organization that provides best practices and strategic advice to many of the nation's hospital systems, points out that low-risk patients (meaning healthy patients who may or may not have one well-managed chronic condition) are characterized by:

- Limited interactions with a health system;
- Did not see a primary care physician on an annual basis or lack a designated PCP altogether; and
- Desire easy access to health information when necessary.

To make the economics work, these patients are key, and a system must limit per member per month (PM/PM) spend on the key services and keep patients loyal to their health system, which would maintain patients in one's network from year to year. Remote monitoring can help accomplish this relationship.

Another use of telemonitoring can be in the postacute era (the time immediately after discharge from an acute care hospital), where proper telemonitoring can limit the amount of times a home health aide needs

---

[100] Iowa Chronic Care Consortium, "Study Validates Use of Technology—Leveraged Diabetes Telehomecare Strategy to Achieve the Triple Aim of Better Health, Improved Patient Experience and Lower Healthcare Costs," (October 11, 2013), accessed June 5, 2014, www.iowaccc.com.

to go to the house of a seriously ill individual, thus providing a return on investment. Furthermore, telemonitoring can allow us to connect with the caregivers and family members and involve them in the process of tracking a patient's daily activity status, overall progress, and chat\send photos to patient.

Technology giants like Google, Apple, and IBM seek to revolutionize how healthcare is delivered, while recognizing the burgeoning market for future products and apps.[101] In fact, 17 million additional Americans have gained health insurance cover under the Affordable Care Act, while 10,000 baby boomers a day are being added as beneficiaries to the Medicare coverage. A $40 billion healthcare IT market (at last count and may be woefully understated now) has emerged centering on a changing delivery model:

- Collaborating with competitors.
- Committing to mega business investments.
- Development of new therapies.
- Improving efficiencies and outcomes for providers.
- Mobile technology use.
- Personal health treatment for chronic-disease sufferers.

Achieving the federal triple aim of better care, improved outcomes, and lower costs for empowered consumers while engaging them will be the preeminent goal. Training will have to focus more on information skills for a whole new category of professionals, while new reimbursement structures will need to take into account these new deliverables.

The Advisory Board showed a return on investment (ROI) after utilizing targeted remote monitoring (see Figure 3). Experience has taught me that unless such use is indeed targeted, the ROI cannot be as rosy. Of course, remote monitoring can take many forms.[102] Keep in mind

---

[101] Tom Sullivan, "Apple, IBM, Google Hold Keys to Make EHR Data Actionable," *Healthcare IT News* (September 2017).

[102] C. Klersy, MD, et al., "A Meta-analysis of Remote Monitoring of Heart Failure Patients," *Journal of the American College of Cardiology* 54.18 (October 27, 2009).

A Positive ROI for Targeted Remote Monitoring

Access to Real-Time Data Requires[1]
Significant Operational Investment

Service	Cost
Remote Monitoring	$353,000
Care Management	$178,000
Medical Direction/Oversight	$48,000
Project Administration	$20,000
Other Expenses	$6,000
Total	$605,000

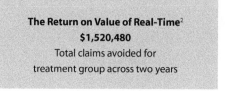

The Return on Value of Real-Time[2]
$1,520,480
Total claims avoided for
treatment group across two years

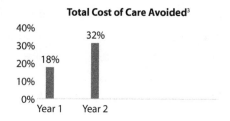

Total Cost of Care Avoided[3]

1) Over three-year period
2) n = 650
3) As compared to control group match cohort

Figure 3: Remote Monitoring ROI (Advisory Board).

Source: Iowa Chronic Care Consortium, "study Validates Use of Technology-Leveraged Diabetes Telehomecare Strategy to Achieve the Triple Aim of Better Health, Improved Patient Experience and Lower Healthcare Costs," available at http://iowaccc.com/diabetesevaluation/, accessed October 11, 2013; Health Care Advisory Board interviews and analysis.

that there are typically two basic questions that remote monitoring tries to ask when it comes to patient care:

1. Is something about the reading wrong?
2. Is something actually wrong?

In March 2015, the Research Kit was introduced by Apple, demonstrating five mobile apps for heart disease, breast cancer, diabetes, asthma, and Parkinson's disease. Before long, thousands of people enrolled themselves in prospective clinical trials. By way of an example, the app for Parkinson's disease quantified the gait, tremor, and voice of a patient, thus furnishing some objective data so the patient can adjust their medications accordingly (true self-management). Since then, more and more apps been released, too numerous to recount here. Suffice it to say that data collection can be frequent and performed during everyday life instead of at a physician's office.[103] I am by no means suggesting that there aren't issues with these apps and major liabilities; however, they are solvable ones.

Wearable sensors will be available for just about every malady, telemedicine visits will be archived, and the number of individuals in the world who have and will have smartphones so voluminous that clearly they will be the new home for the medical data.

Today, it can take up to an average of 2.6 weeks to get an appointment with the doctor while there is a growing list of apps currently in use that allow for video exchange with a licensed physician. Major insurers have begun to cover the visits, which have been priced $40 to $50 range. Payors are getting interested as well for obvious reasons. Dr. Topol points out in his book, *The Patient Will See You Now*, the out-of-pocket costs are comparable to the copays when seeing a physician in the office.[104]

This form of the video chat will include labs, sensor output, physical exam results, and images. Historically, house calls in the 1940s represented 60% of all the visits with doctors, while by the year 2000, they were almost nonexistent.

The following is a list of smartphone functions Dr. Topol envisions not that far in the future:

The medicalized smart phone:

1. Iris/retina/facial expression recognition
2. Voice, breath, lung function sensor
3. Virtual medical coach

---

[103] Quint Studer, *Hardwiring Excellence* (Gulf Breeze, FL: Fire Starter Publishing, 2003), 2–44.
[104] Eric Topol, MD, *The Patient Will See You Now* (New York: Basic Books, 2015), 291–299.

4. Run my labs
5. My selfie physical exam
6. My DNA-drug interaction
7. My block chain
8. My records, labs, scans, office notes
9. PCR draw
10. Microfluidic connection for my labs
11. Show me my data
12. Uber Dr. Housecall
13. My environmental exposure scanner
14. What will my cost be?
15. Ultrasound my body part
16. Run my vital signs
17. Might tell the doctor

We are by no means advising the elimination of the face-to-face interactions of the office visit but a system focused on high quality non-visit care which would work better for many others-and quite possibly for physicians as well. Many providers have already begun the process but usually in an improvised fashion. Kaiser Permanente is proud of the fact that 52% of more than 100 million of its patient encounters each year are now "virtual visits."[105] It does spend about 25% of its $3.8 billion capital budget on information technology—no small figure, but to get started here does not have to break the bank.

Virtual visits basically involve secure email and video interactions and can be as time efficient as one desires. But they are convenient, and it remains our position that virtual visits will grow one's market share by simply providing what most patients crave—easier access and effectiveness. Payment options are evolving, not fast enough for our satisfaction, but smartphone use is increasing.

[105] Alexi Wright, MD, MPH, et al., "Beyond Burnout—Redesigning Care to Restore Meaning and Sanity for Physicians," *NEJM* 378.4 (January 25, 2018).

Making this arrangement a safe one is the knowledge that uncomplicated pathways exist when empirical therapy is appropriate. Duffy, et al even suggest that a patient can "open an app, file a need, answer a few tailored questions, and receive immediate guidance."[106] Fees would accrue to the practice when issues are resolved, and this fact is important, not just for the activity as fee-for-service dictates now.

Other examples include the Providence-St. Joseph's Express Care System deployed in thirty-three clinics in four states, and individuals with chronic needs (over 100 million nationally) would probably derive the greatest benefit.

Now consider this fact again, for it bears repeating. The "meaningful use" metrics that our government put forth regarding information technology in healthcare has "added hours of clerical work each day"; and several studies have shown that this "work after work," which oftentimes occurs at night, on weekends, and even on vacation has increased physician burnout at an alarming rate—twice as high in medicine as in other fields. Furthermore, physicians with symptoms of burnout are more likely to report having made a medical error in the past several months and receive lower patient-satisfaction scores.[107] There is growing recognition that organizations also need to redesign the way that clinical care is delivered. Hence, my juxtaposition of physician burnout with a call to virtual visits. Make sense? I believe so.

A 2017 report on the findings of a seven-year clinical trial funded by the American Society of Clinical Oncology showed that cancer patients lived 20% longer if they tracked their healthcare treatment on a computer.[108] Why not the smartphone now? Our Race to Zero program can easily be supported by an app that allows the tracking of the nine symptoms referable to all diseases, as described in another chapter.

---

[106] Sean Duffy, B.S., et al., "In-Person Health Care as Option B," *NEJM* 378.2 (January 11, 2018).

[107] M. Pangioti, et al., "Controlled Interventions to Reduce Burnout in Physicians: A Systematic Review and Meta-Analysis," *JAMA* 177 (February 1, 2017).

[108] Matt Lashey, "How Smartphones can boost cancer patients' lives," *NY Post* (January 15, 2018). https://nypost.com/2018/01/15/how-smartphones-can-boost-cancer-patients-lives/.

CHAPTER ELEVEN

FINANCIAL STEWARDSHIP

P atients are only now learning how to be consumers by taking baby steps. We need to help them with this transformation, innovation being the key. Consumers need to believe that
healthcare prices are fair and that care increases in value over time. Once
the message gets out that your organization is moving heaven and earth
to truly make them safe and reduce the waste that plagues the system,
they will be impressed by the transformation, the effort. Today, out-of-
network gaming and outrageous charges breed resentment, in the least,
and force so many Americans from participating in their own care based
on affordability issues. Financial stewardship is simply good business.

The Wealth from Health movement is an example of using stewardship as good business. Health systems generate membership by
understanding their consumers and offering a deeper relationship that
builds value over time.[109] It started out decades ago as a rewards system similar to Green Stamps; remember them? My brother and I got
our first baseball mitts in this fashion, and most credit card companies employ incentives based on purchases. It really is the quintessen-
tial motivational program for patients and their families. Credit card
companies continue, I might add, successfully, offering dollars, vacations, and a long list of incentives only limited by their imaginations.

[109] Lawrence F. McMahon, Jr., MD, MPH, et al., "Health System Loyalty Programs—
An Innovation in Customer Care and Service." *JAMA* 315.9 (March 1, 2016).

Wealth from Health members' incentive program is based on earned points for healthy choices and activities. Points become gift cards. Examples that earn points include picking up prescriptions, keeping appointments, choosing salad over fries at local restaurants, keeping track of blood pressure measurements, setting healthy goals, completing surveys, and attending a support group.

Financial stewardship represents another area in which our healthcare system can provide honesty and clarity for consumers who seek price transparency as they wrestle with high deductibles. "If physicians shirk their duty to act as financial stewards when making medical decisions, the end result will be worse health outcomes for the population at large."[110] Dr. Jagsi, et al., showed that a "loss of paid employment after a diagnosis of breast cancer is common, often undesired, not restricted to the treatment period, and potentially related to the type of treatment administered."[111] We do believe that such financial hardships be considered, especially when adjuvant chemotherapy is not believed to be particularly beneficial. Until now, we providers tend not to delve into such matters.

Recently my son, who is an insulin- dependent diabetic, was informed by his insurance company that his present insulin is classified as a "tier 3" medication. Therefore the coverage is minimal, despite the great results it has achieved with his A1c (a measure of glucose control). I am able to help him out so he can continue to take this newer longer-lasting insulin, but, obviously, many families cannot. What is true is that many pharmaceutical companies often times create "me too" drugs in order to capture a percentage of a lucrative market without any demonstrable additional benefit. We simply need to just look at the statin market for cholesterol control. However, my son's insulin lasts

---

[110] Peter Ubel, MD, et al., "Promoting Population Health Through Financial Stewardship," *NEJM* 370.14 (April 3, 2014).

[111] Reshma Jagsi, MD, DP, et al., "Impact of Adjuvant Chemotherapy on Long-term Employment of Survivors of Early-stage Breast Cancer," *Cancer* (April 28, 2014).

much longer than others and, therefore, offers an additional benefit to present-day diabetics.

Promoting competition in healthcare markets sounds great: in general, less competition means higher prices. Proof that this does not exist in the healthcare industry is a provider's ability to charge different prices for the same service. It is our hope that "coordination may foster delivery of the right quantity of care to each patient, while competition may help keep the prices for that care as low as possible. Obviously, what point on the competition-coordination spectrum provides the highest value in terms of quality of care and health benefit per dollar of spending, is not clearly known but an objective to pursue."[112] Wouldn't you agree?

Maybe it is time to start utilizing the quality-adjusted life-years (QALYs) formula so that clinical benefits of interventions can be compared for all diseases. This is being employed by the American College of Cardiology, the Institute for Clinical Effectiveness Research in the United States, and the National Institute for Health and Clinical Effectiveness in the United Kingdom. After all, most patients far prefer whatever time they have left to be "quality" time, rather than a prolongation of misery that leaves them bedridden and too ill to enjoy their remaining days.

An additional challenge of our time is deciphering whether to allocate healthcare resources according to the credo of "doing the greatest good for the greatest number of people" versus "treating everyone equally." Think about it. In other words, if one has a fatal disease, should resources be diverted from "doing all in the face of futility" or divert to those who have a chance for survival with quality. Ethicists have affirmed that this is a valid question to ask. I vividly recall the time I was rounding on a neurology service at Hahnemann Medical College, now

---

[112] J. Matthew Austin, PhD, et al., "Fostering Transparency in Outcomes, Quality, Safety, and Costs," *JAMA* 316.16 (October 25, 2016).

called Drexel, and our team came upon a patient with end-stage Lou Gehrig's disease, ALS. The patient was on a ventilator for a year at that time. On rounds with us was a visiting neurologist from the old Soviet Union. Our attending pivoted to him and asked how they would manage ALS in his home country? I will never forget his answer: "Siberia."

Efforts like Castlight represent steps in the right direction. Consumers and patients who used Castlight Health's online pricing platform saw a significant decrease in certain aspects of their healthcare spending, including a 14% drop in costs for laboratory tests and 13% for imaging, according to a study by the *Journal of the American Medical Association (JAMA)*.[113]

The study focused on the use of Castlight's Enterprise Healthcare Cloud and whether there was a reduction in costs to employers and employees for three common medical services: laboratory tests, advanced imaging services, and clinician office visits. Dr. Neeraj Sood, director of research at the Schaeffer Center for Health Policy and Economics at the University of Southern California, with researchers from Castlight, led the study. They analyzed medical claims from 2010 through 2013 for more than 500,000 employees who had access to Castlight through eighteen employers.[114] Interesting data.

A number of healthcare systems have begun "hospital at home" programs, in which, instead of a traditional admission of a patient to a hospital setting, patients will be taken care of at home by appropriate staff. The goals and critical outcomes to measure success in the case of the Presbyterian New Mexico Health Plan[115] were:

---

[113] Castlight Health Press, "Castlight Health's Enterprise Healthcare Cloud Linked to Lower Costs for Employees and Employers Finds New Study in the Journal of the American Medical Association" (October 21, 2014). https://www.castlighthealth.com/press-releases/castlight-healths-enterprise-healthcare-cloud-linked-to-lower-costs-for-employees-and-employers-finds-new-study-in-the-journal-of-the-american-medical-association/.

[114] Ibid.

[115] Vida Foubister, "Hospital at Home Program in New Mexico Improves Care Quality and Patient Satisfaction While Reducing Costs," *Quality Matters Archive* (Aug/Sept 2011).

- Satisfaction of patients and their families with Hospital at Home care;
- Illness-specific quality measures, e.g. use of ACE inhibitors, ARBs, and beta-blockers for patients with heart failure, timeliness of administration of antibiotics for patients with community-acquired pneumonia (CAP);
- Prevention of healthcare acquired infections and other complications of care;
- Medication management;
- Readmissions to hospital;
- Quality of care transitions; and
- Comparison of variable cost per patient day for *Hospital at Home* versus hospital.

Eligibility criteria included:

- Require hospital admission for a primary diagnosis of chronic heart failure (CHF), chronic obstructive pulmonary disease (COPD), or community-acquired pneumonia (CAP);
- Live within a fifteen-mile drive of the hospital; and
- Covered by the Presbyterian Health Plan.

The movement away from those incredibly expensive institutional solutions, the "edifice complex" (Dr. Topol's term) afflicts those individuals who still see the large hospital building as the most important cog in the delivery of care, has begun as you can observe. Within the first year, patients entered the Hospital at Home program and by June 2011, the number was 439. Of the first 100, only one was readmitted to the hospital within thirty days for the same diagnosis. The average length of stay was 3.5 days compared to 5.4 days the patient with the same diagnosis averaged as inpatients in the hospital itself. Costs averaged between $1,000 and $2,000 a day less, as well.[116]

---

[116] Ibid.

The study by Robinson and colleagues of Safeway's experience with reference pricing for laboratory services adds to a valuable and promising body of work examining additional approaches to contain healthcare costs. By the third year of Safeway's program, they found that the average amount spend per laboratory test by Safeway and its employees was 31.9% less than the amount spend by controls, such that the three-year initiative was associated with $2.57 million savings on laboratory testing, including $1.05 million less in patient out-of-pocket spending.[117]

The opportunity for such a large cost reduction derives from the striking variation in negotiated prices for laboratory services. The price for the most commonly prescribed laboratory test (the basic metabolic panel) ranges from $6.15 at the twenty-fifth percentile to $44.00 at the seventy-fifth percentile.

But for reference-pricing programs to succeed, some work is required on the part of patients, who may have little awareness of price difference across laboratories, especially differences between those in some physicians' offices and in large commercial laboratories. To take advantage of the savings, patients will have to choose the lower-priced laboratories, often instead of the laboratory at the physician practice. Safeway addressed this through announcement of the initiative and by providing employees a smartphone app to compare the price of a test at each laboratory in the network with the reference price.[118]

Financial Returns

Financial return through lower cost per case is imperative in producing a pricing advantage in a consumer-driven market. There is

---

[117] James C. Robinson, PhD, Christopher Whaley, BA, and Timothy T. Brown, PhD, "Association of Reference Pricing for Diagnostic Laboratory Testing With Changes in Patient Choices, Prices, and Total Spending for Diagnostic Tests," *JAMA* online (July 25, 2016). https://jamanetwork.com/journals/jamainternalmedicine/fullarticle/2536187.

[118] Paul Ginsburg, PhD, "Consumer-Oriented Approaches to Cost Containment," *JAMA* (September 1, 2016).

a need to identify high- and low-value care, and choose the former where evidence can demonstrate. Physicians have a moral obligation to be aware of the costs incurred by their patients following their decision making.

Patients are learning to become consumers slowly, but will need considerable help in this transformation. Coordination of care through patient navigation should foster better delivery of the right quantity of care, while competition may help keep the prices for that care as low as possible. Perhaps the QALYs formula or similar tool can be used to compare the clinical benefits of interventions for all diseases.

QALYs in use now:

- American College of Cardiology
- Institute for Clinical Effectiveness Research in The United States
- National Institute for Health and Clinical Effectiveness in the United Kingdom

Pharmaceuticals Affordability Initiatives

Pharmaceuticals Affordability Initiative options are measures that may seem draconian to the pharmaceutical companies, but many experts believe the outrageous expense for medications amounts to approximately 5% of the close to $1 trillion per year of waste in our current healthcare system.[119] This should make your blood boil. The cost of pharmaceuticals is also unsustainable because a significant segment of the population (the elderly) take many medications at one time and are on fixed income. The choice of having money for food or rent will always trump medications, and this predominant factor

---

[119] Nikhil R. Sahni, Anuraag Chigurupati, et al., "How the U.S. Can Reduce Waste in Health Care Spending by $1 Trillion." *Harvard Business Review* (October 13, 2015). https://hbr.org/2015/10/how-the-u-s-can-reduce-waste-in-health-care-spending-by-1-trillion.

keeps more than 50% of all patients unable to take their prescribed medications due to affordability. In fact, they don't even fill the prescriptions.

Possible solutions can include:

- The federal government to allow a subset of payers to join together, commit to a broad treatment strategy as part of a public health campaign, and obtain lower prices.
- The federal government to conduct the price negotiation and purchase large quantities of the pharmaceuticals to make the prices more affordable.
- The government can use its own facilities or commission other manufacturers to make the pharmaceutical without regard to the manufacturers' patents.

Look, manufacturers of pharmaceuticals should be able to make a profit as clearly they need to recoup costs, invest in new research, and after all, they are a business. But the era of mutual understanding and transparency has come.[120]

CVS is a pharmacy chain, a dominant pharmacy benefit manager (PBM) while Aetna is a large insurer, offering health plans for Medicare beneficiaries, as well as serving the employer market. They both sponsor Medicare prescription drug plans. The less sanguine belief is that the merger will "encourage PBMs and pharmaceutical manufacturers to charge higher list prices to capture a portion of the rebates as profits."[121] Also, the Affordable Care Act requires insurers to spend at least 80% to 85% of their revenue on medical care, but, paradoxically,

---

[120] "Levers of Successful ACOs: Transformation to Value Leadership Guide and Strategy Framework" webinar, November 8, 2017.

[121] Austin B Frakt, PhD and Craig Garthwaite, PhD, "The CVS-Aetna Merger: Another Large Bet on the Changing U.S. Health Care Landscape," *Annals of Internal Medicine* (April 3, 2018). http://annals.org/aim/article-abstract/2668212/cvs-aetna-merger-another-large-bet-changing-u-s-health.

that can stimulate higher healthcare prices because it creates a larger base of patients from which to compute allowable profits. Confused?

A more optimistic and less cynical view is that it unites an insurer with a provider (retail clinics) that will likely branch out to more full-service clinics manned by physicians capable of managing more complex chronic conditions. This could achieve more integrated care and value-based insurance design. Studies show that "Medicare's stand-alone drug plans cover drugs less generously than they otherwise would if they accounted for nondrug healthcare spending, increasing the cost of traditional Medicare by over $400 million per year"—as compared to Medicare Advantage plans, which are responsible for the cost of drug and nondrug benefits, and when states shifted provision of Medicaid drug benefits to private organizations responsible for managing non-drug benefits too. Undoubtedly, these clinics would move heaven and earth to prevent unnecessary emergency room visits and hospitalizations and provide convenience (remember, patients crave this). Aetna would win there, as well, by utilizing claims data to identify high-risk or even rising-risk patients to furnish navigation.

Thinking that excessive profit is the sole domain of the pharmaceutical companies is simply not true: "Hospital administrators are oftentimes compensated over a million dollars per year, a device maker stockholders' compounded annual return of 14.95% from 1990 to 2010", and Washington's healthcare lobbying expenditures of $5.36 billion since 1998."[122]

CMS is pinning its hopes on decreasing costs through innovative value based care[123] and while laudable, we still maintain the infrastructure itself of healthcare delivery is a terribly flawed one, necessitating solutions for problems that we have identified as well as solutions looking for problems to solve. Of course, these payment innovations will

---

[122] S. Brill, "Bitter Pill: Why Medical Bills are Killing Us," *Time* (February 26, 2013).

[123] Centers for Medicare and Medicaid Services, accessed February 6, 2018, www.CMS.gov.

ultimately mean very little unless major renovation takes place. That's what this book is all about.

Pharmaceutical Affordability

Tips to lower drug costs include:[124]

- Apply for help in that Medicare and social security have programs for people with limited income.
- Choose a plan that offers additional coverage during the gap (Medicare).
- Consider generics or other lower cost drugs.
- Find out if a Pharmaceutical Assistance Program exists for a particular drug.
- National Patient Advocate Foundation, National Organization for Rare Disorders, Benefits checkup.
- Check out your state's Pharmaceutical Assistance Program.

   Other resources to help:

- Plan Finder Tool (Medicine.gov)or call 800-MEDICARE
- Costco
- Health Warehouse.com
- GoodRx

Financial Stewardship Options

When we talk about financial stewardship, there are many other directions to take and points to be made. A direct result of the Affordable

---

[124] Rena M. Conti, PhD and Meredith B. Rosenthal, PhD, "Pharmaceutical Policy Reform—Balancing Affordability with Incentives for Innovation," *NEJM* 374 (February 25, 2016).

Care Act—and, undoubtedly, one of their goals though perhaps not stated as such—was the onslaught of mergers and acquisitions that major hospital systems and lesser hospital systems engaged in of the past ten years. Ostensibly, the aim was to produce a continuum of care that would produce efficiencies under new payment models. Care coordination was to lead the way. However, many different ideas as to what type of service constitutes care coordination exist. Having already described the Wealth from Health program, it becomes readily apparent that our vision for care coordination included a comprehensive list of activities tied into incentives, community businesses, a CHT, and most importantly, personal relationship(s) that our navigators created with their patients.

What is clear is that coordination may foster delivery of the right quantity of care to each patient while competition may help keep prices for that care the lowest possible. We clearly need a unified approach to an insurance system which is "really several different systems, including moderately competitive private insurance markets for the nonelderly, nondisabled population and a single government payer, Medicare, for the elderly and disabled that largely pays providers set prices on a fee-for-service basis." The promotion of Accountable Care Organizations (ACO) has the potential to undercut the competition by driving consolidation, but it might improve payment efficiency if CMS is allowed to switch from fee-for-service to capitated provider payments.[125] "Policies that attempt to reengineer the health system as we are doing here without changing the underlying financial incentives that drive health spending will ultimately fail."[126] Let us not lose sight of the central fact!

Interestingly enough, international experience suggests that the key to cost control is regulating absolute prices, meaning that value-based purchasing is not necessary for controlling spending. Can you imagine

[125] Katherine Baicker and Helen Levy, "Coordination versus Competition in Health Care Reform," *NEJM* 369.9 (August 29, 2013).

[126] Mark McClellan, MD, PhD, et al., "Competencies and Tools to Shift Payments from Volume to Value," *JAMA* 316.16 (October 25, 2016).

the holy war that would occur if this step were taken by the government? In a *New England Journal of Medicine* article, Dr. Oberlander, et al., described that a value-based payment system "represents a true leap of faith because it is unclear that we have the appropriate measures to accurately, meaningfully, and comprehensively evaluate quality of care."[127]

Dr. Halperin, et al pose an interesting suggestion: "What if insurers considered payment adjustments that are based on changes in the population's health status in time?" What if healthcare systems offered warrantees and trusts, which have been used to manage long-term investments in public goods, thus providing stewardship for valued assets for their patients based on whether, for example, their surgery was successful or not.[128] Frankly, if the surgeon screws up in an operation and has to repeat it, is he or she still gets paid for that second surgery? Hmmm…

All Affordable Care Organizations (ACO) are not the same, as Medicare sets few constraints on the forms they can take. Nearly 1,000 organizations are operating as ACOs, but very few generate significant savings. It could be due to the weak incentives, lack of downside risk, organizational complexity, or a host of other reasons. Sadly, motivation simply exists to maintain the status quo, especially in areas where affluent hospitals are still making a profit, albeit that is becoming smaller and smaller.[129]

Patient Cost Sharing

Increasing patient cost sharing is a blunt instrument: research shows that it can reduce use of both low- and high-value care. Unfortunately,

---

127 Jonathan Oberlander, PhD, et al., "Leap of Faith—Medicare's New Physician Payment System," *NEJM* 373 (September 24, 2015).

128 Neal Halfon, MD, et al., "The Opportunities and Challenges of a Lifelong Health System," *NEJM* 368 (April 25, 2013).

129 Valerie A. Lewis, PhD, et al., "Explaining Sluggish Savings Under Accountable Care," *NEJM* 377.19 (November 9, 2017).

this suggests the patient did not have the information or the skill required to differentiate between the two methods. To date, the methods to incentivize high-value care by the providers has been flawed, but here's the list nevertheless:[130]

- Clinical decision support;
- Clinician feedback;
- New clinical education;
- Patient education;
- Provide pay for performance (P4P) prior authorization;
- Provider report card;
- Risk sharing; and
- Value-based insurance design (VBID)

We believe this function can and has been successfully carried out by our Wealth from Health navigators after receiving appropriate in-servicing on a regular basis. Finding innovative, market-based solutions to expand risk pools and lower insurance premiums, while also providing a robust social safety net, is the key. In 2014, members of America's Essential Hospitals, an organization of safety-net health systems, averaged a 0% operating margin, as compared to the 6.4% average operating gain for all U.S. hospitals. Additionally, about half of all inpatients who were discharged and had subsequent outpatient visits were either uninsured or on Medicaid. Lastly, these same hospitals face competition from for-profit hospitals for those patients with insurance.[131]

We contend the physicians need to disclose the financial consequences of treatment alternatives just like they inform patients about potential treatment side effects. Healthcare costs have risen faster than

---

[130] Carrie Colla, PhD, "Swimming Against the Current—What Might Work to Reduce Low-Value Care?" *NEJM* 371.14 (October 2, 2014).

[131] Jonathan Oberlander, PhD, et al., "Leap of Faith—Medicare's New Physician Payment System," *NEJM* 373 (September 24, 2015).

the consumer price index for most of the past forty years. This growth in expenditures has increasingly placed a direct burden on patients and their families, either because they are uninsured and must pay out-of-pocket for all the care or because insurance plans shift a portion of the cost back to patients through deductibles, copayments, and coinsurance. However, the current reality is that it is very difficult, and often impossible, for the clinician to know each patient's actual out-of-pocket cost, since costs vary by intervention, insurer, location of care, choice of pharmacy, radiology service, and so on. Nonetheless, some general information is needed, and solutions that provide patient-level details are in development.

Whether due to insufficient training or time many, many physicians don't include information about the cost of care in the decision-making process. But discussing cost should be a crucial component of clinical decision-making. Doing so enables patients to choose lower-cost treatments when there are viable alternatives. Patients experience unnecessary financial distress when physicians do not inform them of alternative treatments that are less expensive, but equally or nearly as effective. This phenomenon was discussed when interviewing a cohorted sample of breast cancer survivors who participated in a national study of financial burden. Many women reported discussing treatment related costs with their physicians only after they had begun to experience financial distress. One woman reported that only after she told her clinician, "I am not taking this if it is going to be $500 a month." In fact, the clinician informed her that he could "put you on something less expensive which is just as effective."[132]

Such discussions could assist patients who are willing to trade off some chance of medical benefits for less financial distress. Admittedly, the trade-off between cost and potential benefits is complex and ethically charged. Not including patients in the decision making creates

---

[132] Reshma Jagsi, MD, DP, et al., "Impact of Adjuvant Chemotherapy on Long-term Employment of Survivors of Early-stage Breast Cancer," *Cancer* (April 28, 2014).

patients deprived of the options, and patient engagement merely becomes lip service. Presenting this trade-off to patients also makes clinical sense if we think of the financial costs of treatment side effects.

Discussing out-of-pocket costs could benefit patients by enabling them to seek financial assistance early enough in their care to avoid financial distress. An example: "My husband died, and we were in debt. I was sick, he was sick, I lost my house … then I told my doctor that I could not afford to take medication he was prescribing." One has to wonder whether an earlier discussion about out-of- pocket costs might have prevented the patient from losing her home. The growing body of evidence suggests that cost consideration as part of the classical clinical decision making might reduce costs for patients and society in the long term.[133]

Cost sharing at the point of service often induces poor decision making, as we have noted earlier. Additionally, the lack of shopping by patients seeking and choosing a service on the basis of cost likely contributes to high prices. Making last-minute decisions while stressed clearly is not the best way to proceed. "Along with evidence-based decision support built into EHRs today, technology companies will (provide) handheld device applications aimed at reducing low-value care at the point of clinical decision making."[134]

In fact, patients must learn how to become consumers, and we need to help them with this transformation. Innovation is the key. Consumers need to believe that properly administered healthcare increases in value over time. We have network "gaming," outrageous charges to insured patients (to cover self-pay or bad debt), which breeds resentment at best. It is our contention that, ultimately, such a process is simply good business. The bottom line, however, is that financial return through

---

[133] National Academy of Science, "Best Care at lower Cost: The Path to Continuously Learning Healthcare-America" (2016). Accessed April 26, 2017, www.nationalacademies.org.

[134] Carrie Colla, PhD, "Swimming Against the Current—What Might Work to Reduce Low-Value Care?" *NEJM* 371.14 (October 2, 2014).

lower cost per case is imperative to produce a pricing advantage to the consumer-driven market.

Additionally, we can all agree that the goal of a high-performing healthcare system is to deliver care that improves the health of populations and of course individuals. "United States begins with a challenge: its population is sicker and has higher mortality than those of other high-income countries." Interesting enough, the United States has been slower than others to reduce the "mortality amenable to healthcare," a metric not often referred to but invaluable nevertheless.[135]

I cannot underscore these points too much. With deductibles climbing through the stratosphere and hospital enterprises receiving fewer and fewer governmental subsidies and dollars, the issue of cuts in order to be competitive, simply remain solvent, hold on to slim net profits, has never been more important. *The issue at hand is cost per case.* Over the past few years, most of our administrative staff listened to dozens of presentations given by consultants on how to save money. None of them were physicians with intimate knowledge of the real "waste" issues ($1 trillion worth), but all fixated on wringing out the dollar savings obvious to their naked eye, the lowest hanging fruit.

Let's recap for a moment:

Redesigning both graduate medical education and postgraduate education through the framework of a High Value Care Center, which provides a new generation of physicians with the tools required to assess, test, and improve delivery of care by attacking the trillion dollar a year waste in the healthcare system. After over thirty years of instructing medical residents and students (over 500 for the former and 1,000s for the latter) in the facets of internal medicine, it is high time that we train "change agents" by adopting past rubrics that are still applicable: for example, a good history and physical, while engaging in a high-value care versus low-value care paradigm shift.

---

[135] Eric Schneider, MD and David Squires, MA, "From Last to First: Could the U.S. Health Care System Become the Best in the World?" *NEJM* 377.10 (September 7, 2017).

Embedding a national award-winning patient navigation program into care redesign serves to provide enhanced care coordination outside the confinements of the hospital walls. The list of necessary activities that our patients and their families need to "coordinate" all of the responsibilities given them by their providers is the glue that holds their care together. Again, providing help here is paramount, but will not produce a direct net-cost savings in most cases. However, such utility is sacrosanct to a well-functioning network committed to eliminating waste in the system.

Creating a Community Health Trust to right-size and leverage allocation of resources in the community and to help level the playing field for all patients within our catchment area where social determinants play a significant role in their poor health. Expecting all of our patients to follow our medication instructions when many cannot afford to heat their apartments, buy fruits and vegetables, stroll in a safe neighborhood, flee from a violent spouse, and so on reflects a huge disconnect that I'm afraid afflicts our profession on a daily basis. This is not to say that all physicians are oblivious to their patients' plights, but physicians are generally addressing problems that they can readily solve, while social determinants have been generally considered outside their purview. Until now!

Embrace the era of personalized healthcare, but understand its true value lies in adopting the panoramic view of the individual; as previously noted, adding the metabolomics, microbiomics, physiomics, exomics, anatomics, and proteomics to the current genomics, epigenomics, and transcriptomics discussion is paramount. It is well-known that the EHRs have a rich database of clinical information. "Algorithms will be developed to identify patients with disease risk factors (e.g., for patients with diabetes and elevated LDL cholesterol levels not taking a statin) or to apply pharmacogenetic guidelines to assist with drug selection and administration."[136] There is no question that primary care providers

---

[136] Larry L. Jameson, MD, PhD, et al., "Precision Medicine—Personalized, Problematic, and Promising," *NEJM* 372.23 (June 4, 2015).

will have a challenging role in precision medicine. The stand on the front line and better biomarkers will be needed to assist with disease detection. Examples include imaging to detect Alzheimer's disease,[137] circulating tumor markers,[138] as well as biomarkers for concussion.[139] However, a big however, there exists more financial incentives to create new drugs today instead of diagnostic tests. It is simply more lucrative, and I suspect not even close.

Engage in practice transformation by turning the page on past/ current outdated methods of care delivery and finally deliver the often promised consumer-centric one. Studies casting doubt on the cost effectiveness of the yearly physical exam (10% of all Medicare spending), access issues, millennial mindsets of instant gratification, and a technological boom all generations are enjoying, all cry out for new ways to care for individuals. More than half of all office visits to a primary care physician are unneeded while pharmacists in Alberta, Canada have demonstrated uncanny ability to titrate hypertensive medications for customers at their stores. Unheard of years ago.

Putting the Patient First

Understand the patient's wishes first before putting in place a plan of action that makes assumptions that are yours, but not necessarily theirs. Our profession, sad to say, has always presumed to know what is best for our patients. Such hubris often comes with severe conflict of interests thrown into the mix. "If one is a carpenter, everything looks like a nail." I am reminded of what a sagacious rabbi once said at a funeral

---

[137] J.O. Rinne, D.J. Brooks, et al., "PET Assessment of change In Fibrillar Amyloid-beta Load in Patients with Alzheimer's Disease," *Lancet Neurol* 9 (2010): 363–372.

[138] Sarah Jane Dawson, F.R.A.C.P., Ph.D., et al., "Analysis of Circulating Tumor DNA to Monitor Metastatic Breast Cancer," *NEJM* 368 (March 13, 2013).

[139] R. Siman, et al., "Evidence That the Blood Biomarker SNTF Predicts Brain Imaging Changes and Persistent Cognitive Dysfunction Mild TBI Patients," *Front Neurol* 4 (November 18, 3013). https://www.ncbi.nlm.nih.gov/pmc/articles/PMC3831148/.

I attended of someone who died in his fifties: "A life in many ways is like a good book; it is not judged on the quantity of pages but on the quality of the words." Living until 100 years of age is no bargain if the individual suffered terribly from failing health during the last decade or two.

Be creative with initiatives that begin by placing the patient first. Four individual programs we have are all based on doing just this.

1. Reduce symptoms if no cures are in sight, thus eliminating chemotherapy, radiation, or surgery and substituting with relatively benign palliative therapies.
2. Work with the caregivers; there are over 42 million Americans serving in this role according to last count.
3. Reward people to self-manage their diseases after showing them how, as loyalty and reward programs have demonstrated their value and utility for many years.
4. Help eliminate environmental toxins after visiting patients' homes, affecting change.

You get the point? On a personal note, there've been many times when attempting to introduce creativity into the healthcare field when my ideas have been dismissed at first, only to prevail upon reintroducing them at a later date. Timing is always a factor.

Innovate, experiment, and transform like an award-winning chef does with a recipe until the clinical results honors your patient's wishes and Osler's amazingly applicable theory of disease. In order to truly construct solutions to healthcare waste or disabling disease, for that matter, one must "constantly look for the causes or etiologies," as we say in the doctor business. Now, having been born identical twin and as a father of two adopted children, I certainly understand the importance of our genetic makeup (precision medicine), but have also contemplated our environmental importance (social graph) as well, for obvious reasons.

CHAPTER TWELVE

CLINICAL VARIATION

Employers are no longer accepting the status quo as they feel that we in the healthcare system are dragging our feet addressing their concerns or simply and woefully hiding from the basic truth. They have become keenly aware of the large scale waste in our healthcare system, though maybe not aware of the massive waste per year that we are waging war on. That is, the waste in our system they sense, but, in my opinion, have no idea of the enormity of the problem. Many have decided to be proactive by sending high-ticket procedures (like coronary bypass surgery, etc.) out of state to tertiary care centers, where they received tremendous discounts.[140] But do you actually believe that traveling far from home is what most patients and their family members truly desire?

Point of fact: the majority of physicians still believe that what they do is backed by solid science and their diagnostic and treatment decisions reflect the latest and best research. Furthermore, their clinical judgment is well beyond any reasonable doubt. We must question these beliefs because they are based more on faith than on facts. Unfortunately, only a fraction of what physicians do is based on solid evidence from Grade A, randomized, controlled trials; the rest is based instead on weak or no evidence and subjective judgment. When scientific consensus exists on

---

[140] Brie Zeltner, "Walmart to Send Employees to Cleveland Clinic for Heart Care," *The Plain Dealer* (October 12, 2012).

which clinical practices work effectively, physicians only sporadically follow that evidence correctly (clinical variation).

Medical decision making itself is fraught with inherent subjectivity, some of it necessary and beneficial to patients, but some of it flawed and potentially dangerous. For these reasons, millions of Americans receive medications and treatments that have no proven clinical benefit, and many fail to get care that is proven to be effective. Quality and safety suffer, and waste (trillions worth!) flourishes. Why are so many physicians making inaccurate decisions in their medical practices? It is not because physicians lack competence, sincerity, or diligence, but because they must make decisions about tremendously complex problems with very little solid evidence available to back them up.

Even the most experienced physicians make errors in diagnosing patients due to the cognitive biases inherent in the human thought processes. These subjective, "nonscientific" features of physician judgment work in parallel with the relative scarcity of strong scientific backing. One could accurately say, "Half of what physicians do is wrong," or "Less than 20% of what physicians do has solid research to support it." Although these claims sound absurd, they are supported by research. Yet these claims are rarely discussed publicly, and reiterating this subject matter draws ire from many in the medical community as David Nash, MD, et al., did with their seminal 2010 publication, *Demand Better*, an excellent read.[141]

Most physicians practice in a virtually data-free environment, devoid of feedback on the correctness of their practice. They know very little about the quality and outcomes of their diagnosis and treatment decisions. There is the rub, and without data indicating that they should change what they're doing, physicians continue doing what they've been doing all along. And clinical knowledge generated by randomized, controlled trials takes far longer to reach the front lines of medical care than most people realize. Turning basic scientific discoveries into

---

[141] David Nash, MD, et al., *Demand Better: Revive Our Broken Healthcare System* (Bozeman, MT: Second River Healthcare Press, 2011).

innovative therapies—from "laboratory bench to bedside"—can take up to seventeen years. Unimaginable, but true.

Another realm of physician decision making that is rife with non-scientific influence is diagnosis. There's a whole body of research on flaws in the diagnostic decision-making process, from which we know that as many as 15% of all diagnoses are susceptible to biases. Physicians frequently base their decisions on shortcuts, such as the actions of the average practitioner ("if everyone is doing it, the intervention must be appropriate"); the commonness of the disease ("if the disease is common, we have no choice but to use whatever treatment is available"); the seriousness of the outcome ("if the outcome without treatment is very bad, we have to assume the treatment will work"); the need to do something ("this intervention is all we have"); and the novelty or technical appeal of the intervention ("if the machine takes a pretty picture, it must have some use").

Drug prescribing is another blatant example of medical practice that is often evidence free. Drugs that are known to be effective may work well for only 60% of people who take them. About 21% of drug prescriptions in the United States are for "off-label" use, that is, to treat conditions for which they have not been approved by the U.S. Food and Drug Administration (FDA). That's more than 150 million prescriptions per year. Off-label use is most common among cardiac medications (46%) and anticonvulsants (46%). Here's the real punch line: in 73% of the cases where drugs are used in unapproved ways, there is little or no evidence that they work.[142]

Unfortunately, in America, there is no guarantee that any individual will receive high-quality care for any particular health problem. The healthcare industry is plagued with overutilization of services, underutilization of services, and errors in healthcare practice.

---

[142] Christopher M. Wittich, MD, PharmD, Christopher M. Burkle, MD, JD, and William L. Lanier, MD, "Ten Common Questions (and Their Answers) About Off-label Drug Use," *Mayo Clinic Proceedings* 87 (October 2012). https://www.mayoclinicproceedings.org/article/S0025-6196(12)00683-0/fulltext.

The central problem, as a Rand study has revealed, is clinicians' failure to follow evidence-based best practice guidelines that exist, even though they have been proven to enhance the quality of healthcare delivery. Underuse of recommended services was actually more common than overuse; about 46% of patients did not receive recommended care, while about 11% of participants received care that was not recommended and potentially harmful.[143]

Lastly, the number of available therapeutic options for any given illness multiplies at a dizzying rate, i.e., two dozen approved combinations of antibiotics treatment are available for community-acquired pneumonia, all varying in cost effectiveness. Giving more treatment options to physicians and patients does not mean they will make better choices among these options. Many lead to more clinical uncertainty and variation in physician practice patterns. More tests and unwarranted treatments, exposure to invasive procedures, complications, and error are also part of this picture.

So we have two battles to wage in order to cut out waste. The first is holding physicians to the rules of science that ask them to understand where facts and opinions meet: evidence-based practice and shared decision making. And second, educating our patients and communities that "more is not always better." These are some questions patients should ask their provider:

1. Why do I need the test(s)?
2. What will it/they tell you?
3. What will you do differently once you have this information?
4. Are there other risks of potential harm of the tests?
5. How accurate are these tests?
6. What if I delay the tests?
7. Is there another option with less cost, less harm potential, and less ambiguity?

---

[143] Universal Health Care Foundation of Connecticut, "Overuse, Underuse and Misuse" (March 12, 2014). https://hub.universalhealthct.org/2014/03/12/overuse-underuse-and-misuse/.

CHAPTER THIRTEEN

DIAGNOSTIC ERRORS

What constitutes diagnostic excellence? Recently, a patient came in with complaints of painful joints, abdominal pain, and a rash; she was originally admitted to the surgical service. She underwent laparotomy, where a midline incision was made in her abdomen only to be closed up with no surgical pathology noted. She spent the month on the surgical service with spiking fevers until they decided to move the patient to our internal medicine service; soon thereafter she was diagnosed with Still's Disease. She was subsequently placed on steroids and was discharged within two days, feeling wonderful—a happy ending despite the diagnostic mediocrity.

In developing a solid differential diagnosis (meaning the list of all possible causes of the clinical problem), we can eliminate the burgeoning numbers of diagnostic errors plaguing our healthcare system. First and foremost in the delivery of exceptional medical care, taking a good history, performing a solid physical exam (a drawback of virtual visits but the COVID-19 spike in telemedicine has allowed us to admit this is not always required to provide care), and collecting all pertinent images, labs, and so forth often leads to the differential diagnosis. That list (sometimes short and other times not) of most probable disease entities leading to a particular illness usually sets the stage for a cost-effective process to move forward to prove and then treat the patient as safely and accurately as possible. Get this wrong and the patient's correct treatment plan may be delayed, ignored, or carried out incorrectly—all leading to increased morbidity and mortality.

In fact, the Institute of Medicine has concluded that diagnostic errors constitute a significant issue regarding wastage and injury to patients.[144] Diagnostic reasoning is probably one of the most important attributes of a good internist, but pressures regarding length of stay, frequent turnover, and changes in the emergency department that push to assess, stabilize, and package patients have gotten in the way of teaching this. Clearly, we need to rebuild a culture of "curiosity without constraint," so that the skill set does not disappear entirely.[145] "Yet the reality is that doctors continue to make decisions on the basis of imperfect data and limited knowledge, which leads to diagnostic uncertainty, coupled with the uncertainty that arises from unpredictable patient responses to treatment and from healthcare outcomes that are far from binary."[146] Hence Osler's maxim, "Medicine is the science of uncertainty and art of probability."[147] Despite these truths, we can and must do better!

I felt that this issue demanded its own chapter because of the enormous toll diagnostic errors take on the effort put forth by providers delivering care to their patients. The 18 million diagnostic errors[148] each year needs to be addressed today, but unfortunately, they do not represent a major issue in the minds of most physicians, nurse practitioners, physician assistants, and hospital systems, though they clearly represent just this. There are many reasons for this gap in awareness, including such issues as not understanding or being cognizant of the various biases that can lead a provider down the wrong path, and I include

---

[144] Institute of Medicine, accessed November 6, 2015, www.ihi.org.

[145] Arabella Simpkin, MD, MMSc, et al., "Diagnostic Reasoning: An Endangered Competency in Internal Medicine Training," *Annals of Internal Medicine* (September 12, 2017).

[146] Ibid.

[147] R.B. Bean, et al., *Sir William Osler–Aphorisms from His Bedside Teachings and Writings* (New York: Henry Schuman, 1950).

[148] National Academies of Science, Engineering, and Medicine, "IOM Diagnostic Error in Health Care," (2015), accessed October 4, 2015, www.nationalacademies.org/hmd/Activities/Quality/DiagnosticErrorHealthCare.aspx.

myself here. We briefly touched upon this elsewhere. Maybe even of greater importance is the lack of follow-up or oversight that exists, especially after leaving the residency training program. I often found myself exhorting my residents to "study, read, and inquire" as much as possible during their training years, because no one is going to give a rat's ass when they are on their own. I wanted them to develop those lifelong habits now because it will ultimately serve them well.

As Chair of Medicine, it was incumbent upon me to address the most egregious diagnostic errors that often resulted in extreme morbidity and, unfortunately in some cases, premature death. But these instances only represent the tip of the iceberg, I'm afraid. I would liken them to incidents of carbon monoxide poisonings. Every now and then I treated or became aware of a case of overwhelming carbon monoxide poisoning, almost invariably as a result of a suicide attempt. Through my Environmental Housecall™ initiatives, we found that most carbon monoxide poisonings are low level, mostly from malfunctioning furnaces. But the first rule is to identify a problem, meet it head-on, and devise methods to mitigate it as an issue. The last table describes the DOCASSIST.AI software designed by Dr. Arumugum and my team to help mitigate this problem. A growing body of evidence demonstrates that diagnostic errors are the most catastrophic and costly of all medical errors and the most common. They can be quite nuanced or easily demonstrable, but as a rule, diagnostic safety and quality does not ring bells or lead to alerts of healthcare system administrators.

Two important facts to remember:

- An estimated 12 million Americans are affected each year.
- These errors may account for 40,000 to 80,000 preventable deaths annually in U.S. hospitals.[149]

---

[149] Hardeep Singh, Ashley N D Meyer, Eric J Thomas, "The frequency of diagnostic errors in outpatient care: estimations from three large observational studies involving US adult populations," *BMJ Quality and Safety* 23–9 (September 2014). https://qualitysafety.bmj.com/content/23/9.

It is not an issue of adding more diagnostic test(s), but rather the *correct* ones to the process, as more tests do not necessarily deliver additional diagnostic value. In fact, diagnostic error and diagnostic test overuse only multiply the costs and problems immeasurably. Though we—along with many others, such as the Armstrong Institute for Diagnostic Excellence and Aquifer—are working on software to help ameliorate this problem, there are centers in the United States devoted simply to diagnostic excellence. We strongly urge that centers like this multiply across the country; any monies spent in this area be money well spent, most assuredly.

Additionally, diagnostic errors aren't only the result of poor medical judgment, but can represent a problem of poor coordination of care and poor communication. How many times has the finger on one hand of diagnostic inquiry failed to communicate their thoughts and findings to another finger? What if we backed a simulation lab with virtual patient courses to hone these skills or conceive additional tools to help in this regard? Simply put, the current delivery system is not well designed to support the diagnostic process and that doctors receive limited feedback about the accuracy of their diagnoses.[150]

Some important facts:

- Misdiagnosis-related payments were $38.8 billion between 1986 and 2012.
- Of the 350,706 paid claims, 28% of any pay class were due to diagnostic error.
- Diagnostic errors resulted in death or disability almost twice as often as other care categories.

Based on the CDC.gov website, medical error is the third most common cause of death in United States after heart disease and cancer.

---

[150] David Nash, MD, et al., *Demand Better: Revive Our Broken Healthcare System*, (Bozeman, MT: Second River Healthcare Press, 2011).

Or to put it another way, there are 18 million diagnostic errors each year in United States, and "nearly every person will experience a diagnostic error in their lifetime."[151] The types of diagnostic errors can be classified as no-fault errors, system related errors, or cognitive errors. Why do doctors misdiagnose? Generally, because of rapid decision making, medical emergencies, the increased number of patients per day, and the factors within each type of bias.

Bottom line: we needed unbiased opinion that takes into account only the science and eliminates cognitive errors such as anchoring, availability, or framing effect.[152] A substantial number of diagnostic errors are attributed to flaws in clinical reasoning. They mostly occur in primary care specialties, including emergency rooms. The most common errors due to diagnostic biases include:

- **Anchoring** or sticking with the diagnosis despite evidence to the contrary;
- **Availability** or referring to what comes to mind most easily because you had a patient with similar symptoms; and
- **Framing** or assembling elements that support a diagnosis, such as assuming symptoms are malarial in a patient who recently returned from Africa.

Yet the reality is that doctors continue to make decisions on the basis of imperfect data and limited knowledge, which leads to diagnostic uncertainty, coupled with the uncertainty that arises from unpredictable patient responses to treatment and from healthcare outcomes that are far from binary.

---

[151] Natalie McGill, "Americans will experience at least one medical diagnosis error in their lifetime, report says," *The Nation's Health* 45 (9) E50 (November/December 2015).

[152] Johns Hopkins Medicine, Center for Diagnostic Excellence, Armstrong Institute for Patient Safety and Quality, accessed November 14, 2017. www.hopkinsmedicine.org/armstrong_institute/index.html.

Enough Is Enough

I vividly recall a speech given by Dr. Everett Koop after he had retired as the U.S. Surgeon General, a position he held in such a distinguished manner: "Most malpractice cases that are filed are not really malpractice at all while most true malpractice cases are never filed at all." My personal experience with my own extended family and close friends over the past many years when I have had to intercede in their medical care on their behalf, due to gross negligence, has finally reached the tipping point.

I am going to list these incidents because I wish to chronicle and highlight these occurrences so perhaps I can make sense of them. I am aware of them because of my background in internal medicine, a fact that is even more upsetting because I fear that a large percentage of mistakes are missed, not admitted to by the provider, or buried with the patient.

- A nephrologist failed to recognize that he put my mother into renal failure by beginning her on an ACE inhibitor with bilateral renal artery stenosis (contraindicated). He compounded this by failing to recognize the symptoms of uremia (kidney failure) and treated her for a viral illness until I got to see her and recognized her renal failure. We almost lost her.
- My father-in-law was given a clean bill of health by his internist, despite describing classical anginal symptoms. We then subsequently sent him for cardiac catheterization, which showed triple vessel disease, and he successfully underwent emergency coronary bypass surgery.
- A friend was diagnosed with renal colic (kidney stones) when she actually had sciatica.
- My mother was told that she was suffering from a cervical radiculopathy, when her history of atrial fibrillation made me consider a thrombus (clot) in her arm. The next day, in fact, the arm became cold and pulseless, and she required emergent removal of said clot.

I could go on, but I believe you get the point. Not for one moment to moment, do I believe these mishaps are isolated to my experiences, quite the contrary. Diagnostic centers of excellence with robust simulation and software to aid in the diagnostic process need to be established. We must do better! Soon is not a time. But how?

The quality factor is a difficult one for a patient to navigate. The nuances within the healthcare field in many ways are only known by the physicians themselves. I recall when my beloved mother suffered a stroke while I was a first-year resident in internal medicine in Danbury, Connecticut. I raced to her bedside on Long Island, and for the first time in my adult life, I examined my own parent. Mom had bruits everywhere (sign of diffuse atherosclerotic heart disease) and had been poorly taken care of by an older cardiologist. By the way, this physician had a booming practice. I immediately relieved him of his duties and asked the house staff one question: "Who would you pick to care for your mother if you had to make the choice?" Their immediate collective response convinced me to choose that physician. He took meticulous care of our mother for the next twenty years. Who would know better than the house staff who always know the best? Doctors know who is at the top of the game, but sometimes refer patients to reciprocate to those who send them patients. But if more than one patient returns to your office and complaints about a physician you sent them to, that reflects poorly on you. Put another way, if you prescribe a medication that is not effective, you would not hesitate to take that medication from your list of go to drugs.

Cost shopping at the point of service often induces poor decision making.[153] Additionally, the lack of *effective* shopping by patient (i.e., seeking and choosing a clinician based on cost as well as on care quality information) likely contributes to high prices. Not exactly

---

[153] Michael Chernew, PhD, et al., "Improving Benefit Design to Promote Effective, Efficient, and Affordable Care," *JAMA* 316 (October 25, 2016).

earth-shattering news that making last-minute decisions while under stress is not a good way to proceed.

Redesigning medical education to include a greater focus on value and a patient-focused team approach while training our next generation of leaders will certainly help. Surely the work that we describe here and other forward-thinking places in the United States will take years to effectuate; without motivated and inspired providers to carry on there can be no successful remake of our healthcare system. Our new Healthcare Leadership and Innovation curriculum for medical students and residents has been an unwavering success. Later in the book, you will view the curriculum and some of the participants' evaluations.

Sound economic reasons for medical school curriculum to include courses like our healthcare innovation and leadership endeavor include:

- The institution can boast of a second career center of excellence.
- Creation of the executive physician tract.
- Give students who may not match or be cut out for clinical medicine follow-up career in healthcare administration.
- International repercussions that may benefit the institution.

CHAPTER FOURTEEN

CANCER, BEHAVIORAL HEALTH, PALLIATIVE CARE, POSTACUTE CARE, AND OTHER REENGINEERED PROJECTS

Here, the need to innovate for the sake of your customers by offering affordable, reliable, and accessible products that meet discrete customer needs (i.e., Race to Zero) is critical. The first three (cancer, behavioral health, palliative care), or the "three amigos," often are all mishandled areas in healthcare, but for decidedly different reasons. Behavioral health issues have been the ugly stepchild, though 40% of all chronic disease sufferers experience some degree of moderate depression or other mental health disorders. Funding is poor, outreach limited, and primary care involvement oftentimes absent.

Palliative care is a term that sends physicians and certain demagogic politicians scurrying. The term "death squads" made its way into the vocabulary, making this respected field a mockery for distorted political gain, thus essentially not delivering the symptom control so valuable in the last years of one's life: comfort care and support care. Lost in the discussion, if you wish to call it that, alleviating symptoms is rule number one in palliation. There is much evidence to indicate, short of curative therapy, that symptom reduction and supportive care is desired by most.

Cancer Survivorship Program

Certainly, if there is one disease that merits careful navigation by our Wealth from Health team, it would be cancer. I would venture to say that there is not one family in the United States that has not been touched by this dreaded illness one way or another. Two years ago we lost our beloved sister Diane at age sixty-nine to lung cancer. Diane had retired to Florida and was having the time of her life, when she decided to undergo hand surgery that was supposed to be straightforward. She subsequently developed exquisite pain involving her entire arm along with significant swelling. Her hand surgeon persisted in saying that the surgical site looked fine and prescribed her pain medication. After a full month of this approach without any improvement, a friend assisted her onto a plane and she became a patient at my hospital. While examining her, I noted clubbing of her fingers that was quite obvious. She was, in fact, suffering from reflex sympathetic dystrophy (aka CTS), a condition by where the autonomic nerves produce lancinating pain that would only be relieved by a painkilling injection into the origin of that nerve.

More ominously, clubbing told me that she most likely had lung cancer that was later proven correct by CT scan and biopsy. I'm certain that the cancer had been there for some time and that she would not have been saved even if the hand surgeon had noted these findings. However, his cursory physical exam that missed these findings was indicative of a larger problem today: many providers have replaced thoroughness with expediency. As incomes have leveled off or been reduced, volume increases have become the antidote. The rest is obvious.

Certainly, living life with a history of cancer is unique for each person. Yet there is a common thread true for most, that is, life is different after a diagnosis of cancer. Some common reactions of patients of mine have been:

- I appreciate life more.
- I have greater self- acceptance.

- I feel more anxious about my health.
- I don't know how to cope now that the treatment is over.

The three stages of cancer survivorship that one must be aware of are:

1. **Acute survivorship** begins at diagnosis and goes to the end of initial cancer treatment. Cancer treatment is the focus.
2. **Extended survivorship** begins at the end of initial cancer treatment and goes for the months after. Effects of cancer treatment are the focus.
3. **Permanent survivorship** is when you've surpassed cancer treatment and recurrence seems less likely. Long-term effects of cancer treatment are the focus.

In 1971, 3 million people were diagnosed with cancer. Today there are more than 15.5 million, but of those diagnosed, lung cancer is the leader in deaths; surviving lung cancer today is still an unusual event. Diagnosed cancer statistics include: breast cancer at 23%; prostate cancer at 21%; colorectal cancer at 9%; cervical, uterine or ovarian cancers at 8%; and melanoma at 8%. It is felt that the increased survival rates may be due to four major improvements which include screening tests that may find cancers earlier such as mammography, PSA, colonoscopy, Pap tests; improved management of side effects, which help the patient stay on schedule, and new treatments such as targeted therapy and immunotherapy.[154]

One of the goals of the cancer survivorship program is to follow patients and help them through the post-cancer diagnosis. By all estimates, oncologists and primary care physicians have fallen down here, as the workload and reimbursement concentrate mostly on acute care.

---

[154] Cancer.net, "Survivorship," accessed January 20, 2018. https://www.cancer.net/survivorship/about%20survivorship.

This has proven to represent another valuable role for the Wealth for Health navigators.

Key issues discussed include:

- What key outcomes or endpoints should survivorship programs evaluate?
- Should programs evaluate costs routinely?
- What study designs are the most appropriate methods to evaluate survivorship programs?
- How should cancer therapies, such as ten years of adjuvant endocrine therapy, be followed?
- What is the role of cultural and socioeconomic context on influencing feasibility and applicability of cancer survivorship care?
- How do we optimize wellness and survivors?
- What is the role of self-management programs?
- What models of care lead to better outcomes?
- What are the needs of survivors over time?
- Could a virtual patient navigator program facilitate transitions along the cancer continuum?
- How and when should we have professionals, gerontologists, or other such specialists contribute to cancer survivorship care?

Additionally, survivorship care for the treatment of adult-onset cancers more often focuses on the cancer itself, but doesn't consistently look at the issues of health promotion, primary or secondary cancer progression, symptom management, and long-term and late effects. Models of risk are needed to stratify cancer survivors into different levels of intensity settings for follow-up care. In fact, The United Kingdom National Cancer Survivorship initiative is integrating a stratification process for care of cancer survivors. We would be well advised to follow suit.

Lastly, metrics important to consider when assessing models of care include surveillance for cancer recurrence, screening for physical and psychological psychosocial late effects, assessment of appropriate testing levels, coordination of care with PCP for noncancerous health-care needs, cost of services, patient\clinician measures and satisfaction, and insurance general-health preventive strategies.

It is well-known that the relatively poor health and well-being relative to the higher use of hospital services exists among individuals who have had a former cancer diagnosis when compared with individuals who had no cancer diagnosis. There were increases in heart failure, coronary heart disease, osteoporosis, diabetes, and hypothyroidism. Also, primary care physicians were seen by patients as lacking the necessary expertise in cancer management.[155]

Sadly enough, a study published in *Cancer*—comparing the income of 17,000 patients, including many patients with cancer, between 1999 and 2009—showed that adults with cancer missed on average five weeks of work in the first year of diagnosis, and the family income declined by 20%. No small issue.[156]

Oeffinger and McCabe articulated a taxonomy of models of survivorship care applicable across practice settings.[157] Since then there has been a meteoric growth of survivorship clinics and initiatives in academic institutions as well as community oncology practices. However, there is a lack of a clear reimbursement structure existing for physicians treating survivors, leading to unfair and inadequate reimbursement for these services.[158] Again, save on the trillion-dollar-per-year waste and offer support services with demonstrable need!

---

[155] Mary McCabe, et al., "American Society of Clinical Oncology Statement: Achieving High-Quality Cancer Survivorship Care," *Journal of Clinical Oncology* 31.5 (February 10, 2013).

[156] Jonas A. DeSouza, et al., "Measuring Financial Toxicity as a Clinically Relevant Patient-Reported Outcome: The Validation of the Comprehensive Score for Financial Toxicity (COST)," *Cancer* 123.3 (February 1, 2017).

[157] K. C. Oeffinger and M.S. McCabe, "Models for Delivering Survivorship Care," *Journal of Clinical Oncology* 24 (November 2006).

[158] Mary McCabe, et al., "American Society of Clinical Oncology Statement: Achieving High quality Cancer Survivorship Care," *Journal of Clinical Oncology* 31.5 (February 10, 2013).

Race To Zero™ Program

It is estimated by 2022, that Medicare will become the majority payer of healthcare bills, with the growth from $54 million in 2014 to $60.7 million in 2022. The baby boomers, including me, are getting older, and meanwhile, hospitals are bearing the brunt of payment cuts. Concomitantly, the continuum of Medicare risk models continues to expand. Their future success remains to be seen though the preliminary results are encouraging. However, let's return to our original premise. We know that the overall cost of care for Medicare patients in northern New Jersey, where our hospital is situated, remains 14% above the national average.[159]

My first true introduction to palliative care came when my beloved mother, Joan Ratner, was diagnosed with lung cancer after spending a month in the hospital, suffering from pulmonary edema, end-stage renal disease and sepsis. It was at this point that my twin brother, Jeff, and I, both physicians along with my sister, Diane, attempted to correspond with our mother at her bedside while she was intubated. She let us know that "she had had enough" and wished to die peacefully. When it came time to concentrate solely on palliative care, the same physicians who took meticulous care of our mother for the past twenty years, failed woefully in this area of comfort care. We attributed this to a true lack of understanding of the principles of palliative care.

At the last two facilities where I served as Chairman of Medicine, physicians demonstrated a similar mentality. Our goal was simply to put the emphasis on symptom reduction, which would then open the way to talk further about the goals of care, POLST documents, and living wills. Nine symptoms referable to all diseases during the last months of life were assigned numbers from 0 to 4, and our nurse practitioners worked diligently to lower the number of each symptom to the best of their abilities, utilizing medications or nonmedicinal therapies. Consequently, our Race to Zero™ program was born (see Figure 4).

---

[159] Christopher Waley, et al., "Association between Availability of Health Services—Prices and Payments for These Services," *JAMA* 312 (October 22, 2014).

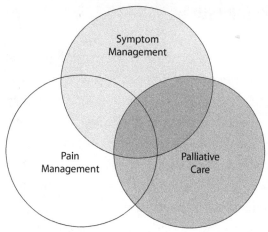

Figure 4: Race to Zero.

RACE TO ZERO

Helping Our Patients with Pain and Other Symptoms

Pain Nausea Cough Shortness of Breath Appetite Ability to Swallow Bowel Movements Insomnia Mood

This symptom-management program was created to emphasize that in a palliative care initiative, symptom control may very well be the most important goal.[160] Through the aggressive reporting, response, and management of symptoms, the program drives better patient outcomes, engagement, and satisfaction, while lowering readmission rates. Symptoms tracked include pain, nausea, cough, shortness of breath, appetite, ability to swallow, bowel movements, insomnia, and mood impression. These symptoms are referable to all diseases at some point and, in many cases, are clearly not mutually exclusive. Again, what do patients truly want, especially if no cure is available?

---

[160] Ravi Parikh, et al., "Early Specialty Palliative Care—Translating Data into Practice," *NEJM* 369 (December 12, 2013).

Cancer Prehabilitation

The emphasis here is to establish the current functional status of the patient and identify comorbidities,[161] and then document baseline activity and exercise levels, understanding that they may affect quality of life outcomes. Once baseline is established, the next step is to identify potential interventions for their ability to improve healthcare outcomes. Examples include swallowing exercises in patients with head and neck cancers, smoking cessation for lung cancer patients, pelvic floor exercises for prostate cancer patients, and so forth.

Categories of treatment during prehabilitation include:

- Patient education\risk reduction skincare;
- Exercise, energy conservation;
- Manual therapies;
- Home program\home health; and
- Referral to other disciplines.

And arrange for completion of the following activities:

- Facilitate all pretreatment physical therapy activities;
- Coordinate the Race to Zero™ program;
- Complete quality of life and SDOH surveys with assistance by Wealth from Health navigators, then referrals if necessary; and
- Smoking cessation referral.

Physical therapy\home care responsibilities include:

- Musculoskeletal evaluation and treatment of impairments;
- Balance\gait evaluation and treatment of impairments;

---

[161] Julie Silver, et al., "Cancer Prehabilitation: An Opportunity to Decrease Treatment-Related Morbidity, Increase Cancer Treatment Options, and Improve Physical and Psychological Health," *American Journal of Physical Medicine & Rehabilitation* 92.8 (August 2013).

- Exercise tolerance evaluation recommendations;
- Cardiovascular recommendations for improving function; and
- Pulmonary recommendations for improving function.

Wealth from Health navigator completes:

- Nutrition assessment;
- Coping skills assessment;
- Depression score;
- Cognitive assessment;
- Home-safety analysis;
- New pressure-sore risk;
- Distressed thermometer and/or caregiver strain index;
- New oral health survey;
- Life fatigue assessment;
- Activities of daily living; and
- Assessment alcoholism screening.

Note: Patients who begin cancer treatment programs in better health and stronger have been shown in studies to achieve better outcomes, stay more active, and feel better.

Help the Helpers Program, a Caregiver Program

After years of taking care of patients while also looking at my own family situation, I wasn't surprised at all to learn that there are presently 43.5 million caregivers in the United States today.[162] Sons, daughters, friends, other relatives, or paid professionals have chosen to help take care of an elderly parent or a very ill, partially or fully incapacitated

---

[162] AARP, "Caregiving in the United States" (2015), accessed October 15, 2016, www.aarp.org/caregiving.

family member. Consequently, our Wealth from Health team cobbled together a program to assist this huge number of overworked and supremely stressed out population.

Our caregiver program has developed at-home surveys that allow the caregiver to provide a better picture of the care environment and patient. These include a depression scale, hearing inventory, Heinrich fall, home-safety analysis, advance directives, a mini nutritional assessment, urinary incontinence assessment, activity of daily living scale, mini mental status exam, speech and swallow evaluation, medication recommendation evaluation, immunization update, and exercise plan. Providing the results to the physician or agency give the clinical team a more accurate assessment then can be garnered by a medical visit.

Caregivers' issues are discussed with the navigator and referrals tracked. These topics can include:

1. Coping and activities for people with dementia
2. Role of animals as caregivers;
3. Cancer therapy nutrition and coping skills;
4. Care and comfort for the stroke patient;
5. Caregiver burnout;
6. Caring for someone with bipolar disorder;
7. Dealing with hearing loss;
8. Developing an organized medication system at home;
9. Long-distance caring;
10. Long-term care planning;
11. Needing and reaching out for a lifeline;
12. Overcoming sadness and depression naturally;
13. Paranoia: know the signs;
14. Six new items on the menu for liquid diet;
15. Tips for managing continence; and
16. Understanding dysphagia or difficulty swallowing.

For the caregivers, it's important they know the following:

1. Are your loved one's legal affairs in order?
2. Do you know enough about your loved one's meds?
3. Does your loved one require care?
4. What kind of home care can help the most?
5. What's available in your community?
6. Who picks up the tab?

Palliative care is a term that can lead certain politicians to poison the well deliberately by describing these dedicated caregivers and palliative care professionals as "death squads." Really? Introducing additional fear and confusion in families who are already deeply saddened and bewildered by their loved one's illness is just cruel. The delivery of symptom control, which is so valuable, is often given short shrift. In these areas, we are forced to innovate for the sake of our customers, offering affordable, reliable, and accessible products that meet discrete consumer needs. A good example would be the Race to Zero™ program discussed earlier.

Palliative Care

Now, cost savings are never the primary intent of providing palliative care to patients with serious illnesses, ensuring the best quality of life and care is paramount. It remains important to understand the financial consequences of serious illness because 10% of the sickest Medicare beneficiaries account for nearly 60% of total program spending. Interestingly, the quality improvements offered by early specialty palliative care and particular symptom reduction may also lead to lower total spending on inpatient healthcare. One study estimated that inpatient palliative-care consultations are associated with more than $2,500 net cost savings per patient admission. It has also has been shown to reduce by 33% overall treatment costs for seriously ill patients.[163] Keep in mind that there is a difference between palliative care and hospice care. Palliative care is appropriate for any stage of a serious illness and could be provided together with curative treatment, which is not the case with the hospice care.

This next point is critical to understand. Major issues in this area include the fact that there can be large information gaps between providers and patients. A number of studies show that the majority of patients with metastatic cancer believe that the cancer can be cured by chemotherapy or radiation. That is because the physicians (in many instances, but not all I might add) choose not to discuss the prognosis with the patient. To be fair, many patients simply don't ask or do not want to know. That is why palliative-care clinicians can remedy this situation by helping patients develop a more accurate assessment of their prognosis. In fact, improved prognostic understanding may explain why patients with advanced cancer who receive early palliative-care consultations are less likely to receive chemotherapy and endure its side effects near the end of life. My mother, mother-in-law, and sister chose this path, and for them, such a decision brought them comfort.

Postacute Care

Postacute care (care after hospitalization) delivered in subacute nursing facilities has become one of the highest cost items in healthcare today and not for all the right reasons. Facilities and physicians have been abusing the reimbursement system by milking it, and despite the fact most individuals rehabilitate more effectively when sent home to receive physical therapy, for example, this option is not always considered, even

---

[163] Thomas J. Smith, MD, FACP and J. Brian Cassel, PhD, "Cost and Non-Clinical Outcomes of Palliative Care," *Journal of Pain and Symptom* Management 38 (July 2009). https://www.jpsmjournal.com/article/S0885-3924(09)00528-4/fulltext.

though it's a mere one-quarter of the cost.[164] With the advent of the federal bundled payment program (BPCI), by which physicians share in savings if there is also an increase in quality (value), this habit has begun to change. But as long as physicians continue to be paid on a fee-for-service basis for every day (and with an eye toward the maximum number of days for full Medicare payment) they see a patient in these facilities, the change will be minimal. Although the BPCI did not provide the overall federal savings expected, it did confirm that subacute days could be substantially decreased without an increase of poor outcomes for patients.[165]

Pediatric Asthma

Another excellent example of a reengineered product is the inclusion of our Environmental Housecall™ program for our Wealth for Health pediatric asthma-control efforts. We sent a number of our navigators to a state-sponsored environmental medicine program (National Healthy Homes Training and Network) that instructed the participants about the indoor pollutants that exist in the home, where to look for them, and how to mitigate them. Additionally, we offered hypoallergenic pillowcase covers and mattress covers, and a dust-mite killer solution for those homes in need.

Mental Health and Comorbidity

It is important to note that depression is the leading behavioral health issue by far and does not often exist in a silo, but accompanies other comorbidities, either as a result of having a chronic disease or as a

---

[164] Robert Mechanic, MBA, "Mandatory Medicare Bundled Payment—Is It Ready for Prime Time?" *NEJM* 373.14 (October 1, 2015).

[165] https://innovation.cms.gov/bpci2-4-fg-evalyrs1-3.pdf.

separate entity. My years in clinical medicine tell me the former is rightfully a huge issue, nevertheless, and quite understandable given the difficult times we live in.

Mental health conditions and substance abuse are some of the most expensive conditions to treat and overlap with many chronic conditions by about 40% on average. With comorbid conditions like diabetes and cardiovascular disease, you have a $293 billion price tag per year alone. We vociferously urge primary care and mobile health be utilized to attend to this area and start the process of adequately addressing this costly issue. We can start with a simple nine-question survey instrument and a depression inventory, along with mobile device connection, once a firm provider/patient relationship is established.[166]

Mental health issues are also critical for assessment in the Sickle Cell Survivorship and HIV/AIDS Survivorship programs, which use many of the same principles previously described in the Cancer Survivorship program. As chronic diseases, proper care and support can result in major changes to the QALY.

---

[166] Barbara J. Mauer, "Behavioral Health/ Primary Care Integration and the Person-Centered Healthcare Home," National Council for Behavioral Healthcare, accessed September 30, 2016, www.thenationalcouncil.org.

CHAPTER FIFTEEN

OUR PRODIGAL SONS AND DAUGHTERS

Much has been written about medical students today and how they differ from medical students of yesterday. I have heard from fellow baby boomer physicians that they are "entitled, lazy, incurious, preoccupied with their social lives, unwilling to take ownership of their patients," and so forth. Not very flattering. The same people blame everything from the Bell Commission mandate (reduction of duty hours brought about after a journalist accused the medical profession of contributing to the death of his daughter because the house staff was too exhausted to properly care for her) to "helicopter parents," whose children were awarded trophies for finishing in last place.

However, it is my belief that after training residents for over three decades, the responsibilities of today's resident are so daunting they are not able to appreciate the joy of getting to know their patients and hearing their stories. Between EMR responsibilities, the extreme pressure to reduce hospital length of stay, and a long list of bureaucratic must do's that boggle the mind, today's house staff are "up against it," in my opinion.

Recognizing this, I spent a considerable part of my academic career relating the joys of medicine to my house staff, always reminding them that they chose the right profession and the many reasons why. In fact, my novel *In a Grain of Sand*[167] recounts numerous cases of mine that resonated within me, not just for the diagnostic dilemmas they posed, but for the patients' personal stories, which were fascinating. And I made certain that every medical student and resident received a copy (gratis!) of this book in order to restoke their interest in medicine, remind them of why they chose the field, and help them see through the murkiness of today's issues to their future satisfaction. William Blake in his poem, "Auguries of Innocence," wrote, "To see the world in a grain of sand…and heaven in a wildflower, hold infinity in the palm of your hand and eternity in an hour…"

Knowing these challenges, and to address the continued low use of evidence-based practice in medicine, we undertook a redesign, see Table 4, in both graduate and undergraduate medical education. In collaboration with St George's University, an offshore academic medical program, JCMC developed a four-week Healthcare Leadership and Innovation rotation for fourth-year medical students that was designed to excite and cultivate an innovative mindset in our future physicians. These medical students were provided with an enhanced multidisciplinary experience in which they received exposure to and partook in high-value care projects, while also participating in leadership meetings at all levels of a large healthcare system. At the completion of the rotation, students documented competencies in:

1. Demonstrating awareness of the changing healthcare landscape;
2. Understanding barriers to care as a result of social determinants of health; and
3. Leading an HVCC project with measurable outcomes by utilizing lean Six Sigma tools, such as DMAIC (define, measure, analyze, improve, and control).

---

[167] Douglas Ratner, *In a Grain of Sand*, (CreateSpace Independent Publishing Platform: 2013).

Table 4: Summary of the four-week JCMC Healthcare Leadership and Innovation course

Week 1	Learn principles of HVCC, population health and interdisciplinary care. Attend as guests VP meetings, QA council and meet navigation staff. 'Business card' interviews with multidisciplinary staff.
Week 2	Choose project area and work with program director to state problem. Use DMAIC process to outline project. Gather data and meet with knowledgeable JCMC staff Home visit with navigators to assess and design mitigation for barriers to care created by SODH
Week 3	Continue project research and provide suggestions for pilots that can be designed to decrease waste or increase efficiencies
Week 4	Presentation to Population Health Council and appropriate SVP of subject area (example, CHF readmission project presented to Cardiology chief and pilot initiated through service line director)

*Modification for internal medicine residents includes six two-week blocks coincident with ambulatory rotations. Residents also presented their project at the annual Research Day in poster-board format. Best project chosen then become a Grand Round presentation.

It is common knowledge that many of today's medical students have been engineers, IT professionals, business consultants, or other types of healthcare professionals before enrolling in medical school. This elective allows participants to meet and interact with others from unique backgrounds who are also interested in improving healthcare with the goal of applying their knowledge of healthcare issues and trends, healthcare personnel, standards, regulations, and population health to optimize the delivery of the core elements of ethics and professionalism and improve practice within any healthcare-delivery organization.

This program also allowed JCMC to effectively implement core Entrustable Professional Activities (EPA), an ACGME requirement to assure core competencies on day one of residency. With the success of the rotation, the program was modified and adapted for the fifty-one residents in the internal medicine program at JCMC. This involvement of students, residents, and professionals in a collaborative intelligence process allowed for creativity, best practices, and declared a call to arms to fix a healthcare system that the next generation will inherit.

One medical student in the program, Leila Javidi, commented: "After four weeks of the elective, what concerns me most is how little I knew about the landscape of the healthcare system before entering medical school. The reality is, unless you are exposed to the inner workings of the system, learning from those directly involved, there is no way to possibly gain this type of understanding. The selective use of articles as a springboard for discussion oftentimes opened our eyes to questions we never knew we had. Things I always thought were simple have now been exposed for their complexity and convolution. While gaining insight into the minutia of healthcare administration, we also had the opportunity to work with visionaries behind the revolutionary Wealth from Health program. Spending time with these individuals has allowed us to flex our innovative minds to practical applications, though vision is not enough. We have to have pragmatic approaches and you have to start from the ground up and take everything into consideration before interventions can be practically implemented. … I am excited to bring this knowledge into a residency and my future career."

CHAPTER SIXTEEN

KILLER APPS AND THE VALUE-ANALYSIS COMMITTEE

An "Innovation Think Tank" would most definitely be a boost for an improved healthcare system. Deep down, we all harbor a secret desire to be creative in some fashion, whether it be cooking, art, music, a great golf swing, and so forth. There are many, and I include myself, wish to be part of this card-carrying club of creatives, especially when being in such a concrete profession. How do we get there? One good way is certainly through technologic advances. New treatments, process improvements, and high-value care initiatives, no doubt. Always making certain to think from the patient's vantage point.

A 2011 report from Susanna Fox from Pew Internet, "Peer to Peer Healthcare," demonstrated the ubiquitous use of social media by those with chronic conditions, perhaps just as important of a trend toward routinely reaching out to others with similar conditions for advice on how to manage their illnesses. In fact, two studies that I am aware of have made it into medical journals: "Perceived Benefits Of Sharing Health Data Between People with Epilepsy on an Online Platform," which was published in the *Journal of Epilepsy and Behavior*, and a 23 and Me study, "Efficient Replication of Over 180 Genetic

Associations with Self-Reported Medical Data," which was published in the *Journal of Medical Internet Research*.[168]

Additionally, hospitals and health systems are already integrating social media into their marketing and patient-engagement efforts. Our own Wealth from Health program is no exception. We need to have a healthcare system that learns in real time, with new tools, how to manage problems better. "Builders rely on blueprints to coordinate the work of carpenters, electricians, plumbers while banks offer customers financial records that are updated in real time. Automobile manufacturers produce thousands of vehicles that are standardized at their core, tailored at the margins."[169] What about us? Medicaid block grants, some would say, could incentivize states to become "laboratories of democracy," where we can see innovation become paramount.[170]

Our gut feeling tells us that it would probably reduce Medicaid eligibility and lower benefits as states try to save taxpayer dollars. In addition, failure to have a continuous sustainable risk pool would be catastrophic in the individual and small business insurance markets. There is no doubt that the Holy Grail here is to find innovative solutions to expand risk pools and lower insurance premiums. We should never abandon a healthy social safety net!

Health systems should adopt a more comprehensive view of accessibility, one that extends beyond a physical access to care. Mobile apps, telemedicine, health kiosks are the key to the future of our industry. We need to go where our patients are, where they go about their lives. "Build it and they will come," the *Field of Dreams* mantra, no longer applies. Why not? A hospital of 300 beds has an average, according to

---

[168] John Sharp, "A Look at Social Media in Healthcare–Two Years Later," (May 21, 2012), eHealth, http://ehealth.johnwsharp.com/2012/05/21/a-look-at-social-media-in-health-care-two-years-later-ihealthbeat-post/.

[169] "Transformation of Health System Needed to Improve Care and Reduce Costs," Health and Medicine Division of the National Academy of Sciences (September 6, 2012).

[170] Lawrence O. Gootin, JD, et al., "The Affordable Care Act—Moving Forward in the Coming Years," *JAMA* 317.1 (January 3, 2017).

the Advisory Board, of 17,000 inpatients per year, 30,000 out-patient visits, and 170,000 patient communications per year. These statistics are quite revealing. Over 90% of all patient connections exist outside the physical hospital building, which Dr. Eric Topol refers to as the "edifice complex." Still today, larger and larger hospitals are being built, despite these facts playing out throughout the United States. Why? It's simple. Inpatient revenue still remains their bread and butter. I recall a conversation with a hospital CEO who once told me categorically and without hesitation, "Why should I believe in disease management? It will keep fannies out of my beds." My response: "A doctor would never talk like that." But at least he conveyed to me the stark reality of "no money no mission."

According to Wikipedia, a killer application in marketing terminology is: "Any computer program that is so necessary or desirable that it proves the core value of some larger technology, such as computer hardware, a gaming console, a programming language, a software platform, or an operating system."

Billions of dollars in venture capital is making its way here as well. But will they prove effective in healthcare? Helping patients take their medications as directed by an app is a possibility, according to Aaron McKethan, a senior vice president of strategy at RxAnte, but will it help them afford the medications?[171] No. However, the Congressional Budget Office (CBO) estimates that a 1% increase in the number of prescriptions filled would cause Medicare spending on medical services to fall by roughly .05%, no small number when dealing in trillions of dollars spent. But ... Congress would be wise to look at Medicare's "Plan D" spending and understand that, yes, taking meds as prescribed is crucial, but missing some doses pales in comparison to not taking any meds at all due to affordability issues.

---

[171] Aaron McKethan, "The Next 'Killer App' To Cut Health Care Costs: Getting Patients to Take Their Meds," *Forbes* (May 1, 2013).

Providence St. Joseph Health in Seattle is well ahead of the game as they are actively driving innovation in the digital healthcare space with their "Express Care Virtual." Their health system comprises fifty hospitals, 829 clinics, 23,000 physicians, and nearly 2 million covered patients. They view successful digital solutions as economically and clinically valuable to their system. First they learn if they or the market has the application available, and if not, they develop it. There are three key steps:

1. **Entice**. The app needs to be ten times better than what patients have experienced before, otherwise it will not be used, but is intentionally made to look similar.
2. **Engage**. Since healthcare tends to be episodic, how can you make certain that they will come back?
3. **Scale**. The app must provide the following for the health system:
    *   Improved population health;
    *   More efficient use of clinical time;
    *   Protection from industry disruption;
    *   New revenue streams; and
    *   Lower-cost digital access.

One issue that we are struggling with is the need to develop our own apps and incur the expense. At last count, there are roughly 165,000 around healthcare apps today, although a mere thirty-six comprise nearly 50% of the downloads.[172] "Two key data points illustrate how almost all of the apps fall short: just 10% can connect to a device or sensor while a mere 2% sync into provider's systems, and that functionality could greatly improve both accuracy and convenience of data collection. Nonetheless, the growing interest in the use of mHealth apps

---

[172] Ken Terry, "Number of Healthcare Apps soars, but Use Does Not Always Follow," *Medscape* (September 18, 2015). https://www.medscape.com/viewarticle/851226.

for chronic disease management showing encouraging signs of interest, with more than 33% of physicians reported having recommended such and to their patients."[173] It is clear that my millennial medical students and residents rely a great deal on their mobile devices.

Reasons given for proceeding with one's own apps, despite the thousands that are presently in the market, are summarized by Scott Gerber, an expert in the field.[174] A native app:

- Creates a stickier relationship with your user.
- Will provide valuable data can be leveraged and monetized.
- Can increase your Google rankings.
- Can be used without the Internet.
- Can help you obtain a much higher conversion rate.
- Provides the convenience value to customers.
- Can engage a two-way communication.
- Can add value or functionality.
- Align business drivers: revenue, productivity and quality of life.
- Provides user convenience and constant reminder of your brand.

Current and Future Health Apps

Some apps can reduce outpatient costs and improve quality of life and are tied to native initiatives. These can include:

- Race to Zero™
- Behavioral health access
- Cancer prerehabilitation

---

[173] Ibid.

[174] Scott Gerber, "12 Reasons Your Business Should Have a Native App Before 2016," accessed January 24, 2017, www.mashable.com/2015/09/09/business-native-app.

- Cancer survivorship program
- Choosing wisely in low-value care
- Chronic kidney disease prevention
- Community health trust partnership
- Environmental Housecall program
- Financial stewardship
- Help the Helpers program
- Hepatology clinic
- Imaging stewardship
- Improving diagnoses
- Nutrition do's and don'ts
- Observation unit do's and don'ts
- Occupational history taking
- Procedural efficiency
- Renal/rheumatologic do's and don'ts
- Sepsis
- Serial inebriation program (SIP)
- Shared decision making
- Sickle cell stewardship
- Sleep apnea
- Social media
- Super-utilizers: Hospital at Home programs
- Wealth from Health Credit Calculator

Caregiving Apps

- Caregiving
- CareZone
- Caring Village
- CaringBridge

- eCare21
- Elder411
- Lotsa Helping Hands
- Medisafe

Diabetes Apps

- BeatO
- BG Monitor
- Diabetes Tracker
- Fooducate
- Glooko
- Glucosio
- Health2Sync
- MyNetDiary PRO
- mySugr

Miscellaneous Health Apps

- ACC statin intolerance
- Antibiotic stewardship
- Family medical history (Da Pont)
- Johns Hopkins Epiwatch™
- PillDrill

Wealth from Health Apps

- Wealth from Health Credit Calculator
- DOCASSIST.AI

Suggested Future Native Apps

This list is not necessarily complete, nor do all the potential apps carry equal weight:

- Choosing wisely to avoid low-value care
- Clot-busting program
- Discharge efficiency
- Joint Commission (hospital accreditation) benchmarks
- High-value care as it pertains to antibiotic use
- Hyper and hyponatremia algorithms
- Imaging stewardship
- Improving diagnoses
- Mobility/sedation in the ICU
- Perioperative management
- Procedural efficiency
- Pros and cons of placing peg tubes/tracheostomy
- Race to Zero™ program
- Reduce inpatient costs and achieve better results
- Rheumatologic markers
- Sepsis
- Sickle cell management
- Syncope
- Transfusion stewardship
- Value-analysis committee

Value-Analysis Committee

As long as I can remember, physicians have approached the hospital's administration to purchase the latest equipment, arguing vociferously and adamantly it was mission critical to keep up with the newest technology, but they were never asked to deliver a business plan to make their case(s). Today, this is changing. In fact, a number of years ago I saw the term "value-analysis committee," which had been established at the University of Pittsburgh Medical Center (UPMC) to evaluate the cost effectiveness of purchasing the "latest" technology.[175] The constitution of that committee made eminent sense, so JCMC implemented its own version.

Good examples of this type of evaluation include reviewing the tremendously expensive robotic surgery equipment,[176] as well as the use by cancer experts of proton therapy;[177] neither were proven to be more effective for their respective current modalities. Physicians are now mandated to prepare a business plan and make their case to the committee.

Questions that need to be asked in a Value-Analysis Committee include:

1. Is the new technology cost effective?
2. What is the current technology?
3. Should the current technology be eliminated?
4. Why is new technology better than the current?
5. Is there a consensus among members of your department?

Newly uncovered savings comes not just from reduced prices, but from eliminating waste, inefficiency, misuse, and value mismatches of the product, services, and technologies in healthcare.

---

[175] UPMC Life Changing Medicine, accessed August 8, 2015, www.upmc.com/about/supply-chain.

[176] A. Ahmad, et al., "Robotic Surgery Current Perceptions and the Clinical Evidence," *Surgical Endoscopy* 31.1 (January 4, 2017).

[177] D. Wang, "A Critical Appraisal of the Clinical Utility of Proton Therapy in Oncology," *Medical Devices* (October 2015): 439–446.

A case in point: One of our internists wanted to substitute a pigtail catheter for the previously used straight catheters inserted to drain a pleural effusion. His rationale included the following:

1. The older catheter had a higher risk for complications.
2. The new catheter can be left in place longer.
3. It saves the patient a second procedure, which would expose a patient to additional radiation from a CT scan.
4. It saves nursing transport time and reduces length of stay due to the difficulty in scheduling same-day radiologic services.

The Value-Analysis Committee voted unanimously to approve his request and asked him to look at certain metrics and report back to the committee to see if, indeed, his business plan was accurate. Follow-up to the committee showed that the results were good, and the catheter became best practice at JCMC.

CHAPTER SEVENTEEN

THE WEALTH FROM HEALTH KEY STRATEGIES

D ecisions individuals make daily have far greater effects on their health than decisions controlled by the healthcare system. I'm reminded of when I studied for the board exam in occupational and environmental medicine. A strong premise included the fact that, depending on which part of the country one lives, we spend on average of between 90% and 99% of our time indoors. Therefore, indoor pollutants posed a greater danger to our health than outdoor pollutants, generally speaking. Why do I bring this point up? Because, believe it or not, the majority of Americans spend the vast majority of their time making decisions about their own health *without* the benefit of the healthcare system. That's common sense, about 5,000 hours' worth.

Nobody's whispering in their ears about what to do, although our Wealth from Health patient navigators tend to excel in this area by serving as coaches, mentors, and above all, people who care. Let's not make light of this last point. Never in my lifetime has the need been more acute or invaluable. However, whatever side one takes in this discussion, what is irrefutable is that between lifestyle choices and the responsibility of self- managing a chronic disease, more can be done to effect a state of acceptable health than all the doctoring in the world.[178] Think about this fact!

In summary there are four key Wealth from Health strategies:

1. Knowledge of the new American health system (Affordable Care Act, higher deductibles and copays for inappropriate care and poor decisions);
2. Mitigating barriers to care;
3. Health is in the consumer's control, including home safety and compliance with (shared) care plans; and
4. Who to call when you have a question about next steps.

One year ago, I went down to the small conference room of the hospital and sat in front of a computer screen for twenty minutes while the instructor searched repeatedly for my name in a drop-down box so she could begin teaching me how to do computerized physician order entry (CPOE) in the newest version of the electronic record. She couldn't find me—likely because the system searched back only one year, and I had stopped admitting patients. I patiently waited through all her attempts, knowing that the tutorial was useless for me. So why was I there? I received a $10 gift card for my kids' favorite coffee shop. While $10 wasn't going to change my day, I was still rewarded for completing a small task. My time was an easy sell.

Free Stuff

From the days when we bribed our kids to eat a few more peas to the concept of reward points for choosing one airline over another, we love discounts, points, and incentives: free stuff. Twenty years ago, the Wealth

---

[178] Robert Kaplan, PhD, et al.," Adding Value by Talking More," *NEJM* 375.20 (November 17, 2016).

from Health program decided to find out just how far patients could be pushed to get healthy. Emphasizing longer life, less disease when you are old, or lower healthcare costs to your wallet wasn't working. Only 3% of the population did everything right—meaning they followed the recommended guidelines for diet, exercise, stress, sleep, toxic habits, etc. Humans are not good at working for long-term goals. We don't "feel" into the future; short-term gratification is more rewarding. And no, doing the right thing simply because it is "right" (a common physician standard) wasn't working. But could we really change our health choices to earn free stuff?

Take these three examples.

1. You feel pretty good, but a doctor tells you, "Stop smoking, lose weight, and take these two pills twice a day for the rest of your life so you don't have a stroke in ten years. Oh, and come back in a week to see if the pills work, but call if you have any of the annoying side effects we discussed." Sound familiar?

    Common response: "I've got at least five years to think about it. I'll lose a few pounds and then go back or wait till I'm sick. That will save me the hassle of doctor visits, pharmacy reminders, and dollars out of my pocket. I've got enough on my plate."

2. You've had a cough for a week and haven't been sleeping well until this morning when you slept through the alarm and decided to take a day off work, thinking that would help especially since it was the Friday before a three-day weekend. Only on Sunday do you remember your company's "Friday before" rule, so you will need a doctor's note to get paid for that sick day you took.

    Common response: You've got a $50 emergency room copay, but that's worth it not to lose out on a day's wages. And besides, if it runs long, the football game will likely be on in the waiting room. Four hours later, your team has lost, but you have a scribbled note you can hand in on Tuesday.

3. And this final example. You are hungry and tired. The drive-through is open.

Common response: "What's one more bacon cheeseburger and fries in a lifetime of meals? Tomorrow is a good day to start getting healthy."

What could change these common responses to promote health?

The Wealth from Health Reward Points Program

Let's bring in the Wealth from Health (WfH) reward points program and change the dynamics. WfH takes common chronic disease states and preventive-medicine guidelines and turns clinical expertise into journeys to optimal health. Learning how to stay well, manage chronic disease, prevent complications, and play by the new rules is part of the game plan. The goal? *A healthier population at a lower cost.*

Health journeys are broken down into specific tasks for which patients enrolled in our program receive points. These tasks range from general—such picking up scripts on time, wearing seatbelts, getting a flu shot, watching videos, choosing healthy food choices—to more specific tasks, such as attending support groups, going through prehabilitation therapy before starting chemotherapy, completing a shared decision making module prior to surgery, or caretakers completing risk assessments for their loved ones. These points convert to gift cards (the most popular are for a large supermarket chain).

Patients complete a stratification tool every six months that quantifies barriers (socio economic, disease burden, cultural beliefs, personal likes and dislikes, access to healthy choices, etc.) so that the proper, most efficient help (navigation, enrollment into governmental or community services) can be provided. We also watch for the patient's risk level to trend downward and quality of life (the SF-12 survey) upward as they move through the program.

WfH collaborates with the community and creates as many win/win situations as possible so that vendors participate by offering discounts for healthy choices (more customers for them) and they spread the news about what WfH is doing for the community (translates to new members and a healthier community). We also hold an annual Community Health Trust meeting so that the players get to know each other and (hopefully) stop duplicating services so that they can preserve their niches.

Crucial to any comprehensive plan to revamp healthcare as we know it is an easy-to-follow summary of progress to date, including but certainly not limited to:

1. Risk stratification/navigation mapping;
2. Patient navigator workload;
3. Patient navigator-patient ratio;
4. Specific local programs;
5. Program enrollment/navigation; and
6. Program outcome.

Patient Navigators Are Key

Patients or families sign up to be part of the rewards program and they receive points they can convert to gift cards when tasks are completed. It is a voluntary program and free to be a member. You receive a one-on-one visit with a health system employee called a navigator. Navigators are personable and know the system; think informed professional friend.

At the first visit, you complete a stratification tool that quickly identifies your barriers to health: disease burden, cultural beliefs, time management, access to transportation, depression, physical disability, language difficulties, etc. Notice that *burden of disease* is only one barrier to health; most are what are now termed socioeconomic determinants of health (SDOH). These range from a traveling executive consultant without a true home base or time for an office visit to a non-English-speaking homeless ex-felon. SDOH are *not* a new way to say "poor"; everyone has some barriers to care that impact our health. And health remains the goal.

Together, you and your navigator plot out what's important to you (also called self-management goals) so you can earn reward points and set the course for your journey to optimal health. Every step must be doable and timely, available in the community, aligned with your skill set, and short term versus long-term. Simply complete the task and get the points!

Reward Points

The number of points (or credits) is on a WfH template that includes:

- an online educational session;
- compliance with medications;
- office visits;
- preventive care visits;
- following high-value care instructions;
- completing a quality-of-life survey;
- understanding advance directives;
- completing online risk assessments; and
- reaching personal goals (as set with navigator help), which might include: no missed work days, taking a planned three-day vacation, signing up for social programs, buying a bike helmet, etc.

Every 100 points means a $10 gift card.

When first trialed at a Pennsylvania factory, the reward dollars were shared, and people from the president of the facility to front-end staff lined up around the block to show their proof of completion, such as a receipt for a bike helmet or a note from their doctor that they had their tetanus shot. It was manual back then, but it's now attached to an IT platform for tracking points and redemption.

Local Discounts

In addition to points, discounts that promote healthier choices and habits are also available. WfH showcases the principles of population health by moving outside the walls of the hospital to engage the businesses that surround the hospital. Businesses need customers, and people need to take better care of their health. Win/win. So local vendors partner with the WfH program to offer members discounts when they show their WfH cards.

Common examples of discounts are: 10% off a veggie pizza (not pepperoni), no initiation fee when joining a local gym, WfH coupons from a local supermarket for fresh vegetables, or 20% off a spa massage.

Health Education

Points and discounts go hand in hand with health education, and learning how to follow the new healthcare rules is also thrown in. Let's look at the previous examples again, and see if we would move a bit further on the journey to better health by using the WfH formula and reward points.

1. "I've got at least five years to think about it. I'll lose a few pounds and then go back or wait till I'm sick. That will save me the hassle of

doctor visits, pharmacy reminders and dollars out of my pocket. I've got enough on my plate."

20 points for joining WfH and meeting with your navigator.

10 points for watching a video on the effects of blood pressure (BP) on your brain and heart.

5 points for each time you record your BP at your supermarket in the first month of membership.

10 points for making a follow-up appointment with your primary care doctor.

10 more when you keep that doctor's appointment.

20 points for picking up your medication.

10 points for watching a fifteen-minute stop smoking video

20 points for setting a "stop smoking" date.

100 points when you are cigarette free for one month.

Your initiation fee was waived when you decided to join the local gym.

Result: now you may have earned a $10, $20, or $30 gift card just for doing small tasks of your choice.

2. You've got a $50 emergency room copay, but that's worth it not to lose out on a day's wages. And besides the football game will likely be on in the waiting room. Four hours later, your team has lost, but you have a scribbled note you can hand in on Tuesday.

    20 points for joining WfH and meeting with your navigator.

    10 points for watching a video on reasons to go or not go to the ER.

    10 points for completing a risk assessment that indicates diabetes might be in your future.

    20 points for taking a supermarket tour learning to read labels and cut back on sugar.

    20 points for watching a video on sleep disorders.

10 points for making a follow-up appointment with your primary care doctor.

10 more when you keep that doctor's appointment.

Got a 10% discount on your veggie pizza.

Result: now you may have earned a $10, $20, or $30 gift card just for doing small tasks of your choice.

3. "What's one more bacon cheeseburger and fries in a lifetime of meals? Tomorrow is a good day to start getting healthy."

    20 points for joining WfH and meeting with your navigator.

    10 points for setting a goal to stop going to McDonalds for a week.

    30 points for trying out the local gym with a free session.

    50 points for getting your vaccines up to date at your local pharmacy.

    30 points for having a home-safety environment checkup with your navigator.

    10 points for replacing all the batteries in your smoke alarms.

    Got a 10% discount on your meal by having a salad with that steak.

Result: now you may have earned a $10, $20, or $30 gift card just for doing small tasks of your choice.

We believe we have barely scratched the surface on ways to utilize these credits. Once you get in the habit, there are points for weekly, monthly, and annual goals and for many specific tasks to reach them, which can be quickly accumulated. And you also have an informed friend (the navigator) you can call when the choices or system seems chaotic.

So what about the cheaters? You say "I didn't hit McDonalds this week. Score me ten." The program purposely has tasks that are self-attestation. Just being part of a program has patients understanding their role in their own health. If they choose to game the system, we have still slyly imparted the importance of that task (education!). That's enough of a win for the WfH team.

The following algorithm (see Figure 5) shows the breakdown by site, team member (including patient and community), and services the WfH program puts in place for a patient with asthma, a common yet potentially fatal disease among urban adults and children. Similar algorithms have been designed for chronic and acute diseases that present to JCMC. Rapid cycles of improvement hone these recipes to meet changing demands and population needs.

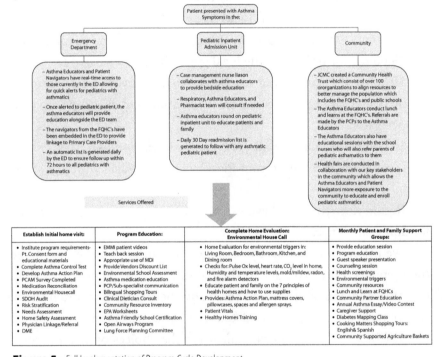

Figure 5: Full Implementation of Program Cycle Development.

The New Health Model

A model that diagnoses a disease and prescribes a course of therapy (the core of current medical school education) is different than the Wealth from Health model that most effectively helps patients to self-manage their health (where possible) and make the necessary behavioral adjustments to live free from the complications of a disease. It makes the physician/patient relationship not about *disease*, but rather more about *health*. Think if Kodak was not about cameras, but about images (a concept that would have prevented bankruptcy if the company had been smarter).

Physicians simply do not have the time or the expertise to excel at all parts of this journey: diagnoses, treatment, navigation, and support of patient-set goals. Their time is much better utilized when navigators are part of team medicine. Team medicine is driven by the need for comprehensive health journeys, which is where is where the Wealth from Health model of care excels.

Importantly, the skill set for this team of navigators is close to that of the ultimate salesperson—friendly, engaging, and smart. Part of the financial success of the program was using college graduates, regardless of field, as navigators. Figure 6 show how cost was impacted as participants made less use of ER visits and inpatient stays when comparing post and pre WfH enrollment. The need for inherent medical knowledge was obviated by the wealth of online resources and support groups managed by the team. Not needing nurses or social workers to take on this role kept those professionals practicing to the top of their degrees and let the navigators do their magic with knowledge of the system, not the disease.

As an aside, over the thirty years that I have been instructing medical students and residents in internal medicine residency programs, whenever discussions turned to care coordination, prevention, or more mundane social issues, and away from the esoteric diseases and "zebras" (highly unusual cases), I could see their collective minds wander—as if those issues were not at all fascinating or vital to health. Physicians will not solve healthcare by taking on the role of navigator. Instead, education must train them to lead and manage teams as core to providing patients with the tools and answers required for optimal health.

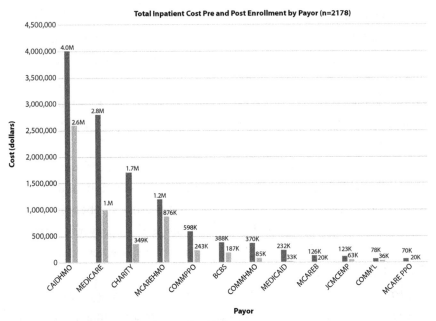

Figure 6: Total Inpatient Cost Pre and Post Enrollment by Payor.

The Science of Navigation

The business model for healthcare must incorporate the science of navigation. Navigators establish a personal connection and rapport with their patients; they are integral in establishing a trust, a comfortability. They must "activate" the patient to self-mange themselves, no small task.

And this connection cannot be telephonic, a current mainstay of large insurers and systems as best demonstrated by the failed Medicare Health Support Disease-Management Pilot Program that included an intervention group and a control group.[179] The tested telephone support, which scaled easily, failed to reduce costs; it actually increased them, leading to a premature closure of the study. Three reasons it failed:

---

[179] Nancy McCall, Sc.D., et al., "Results of the Medicare Health Support Disease-Management Pilot Program," *NEJM* 365 (August 11, 2011).

1. A personal contact was not established.
2. The "navigation" was not seen by the patient to be connected to the physician.
3. Telephone calls are a disembodied tool that fail to elicit patient responses that translate to appropriate follow-up care, the gold standard for success.

Wealth from Health navigators always connect with the patient in face-to-face introductions and follow-up visits. Subsequent telephone calls and texting are then received by patients as a friendly contact and not as a check-off list. Communication ordination by the navigator with the physician is mandatory to deliver the same messages. This tie-in with the patient's physician allows for coordinated care and builds trust between partners. From a fiscal point of view, well-navigated care reduces redundancy, prevents missed opportunities for early and

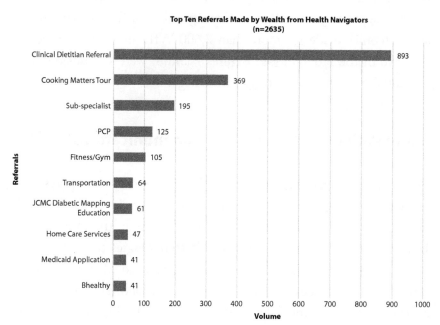

Figure 7: Top Ten Referrals Made by WfH Navigators.

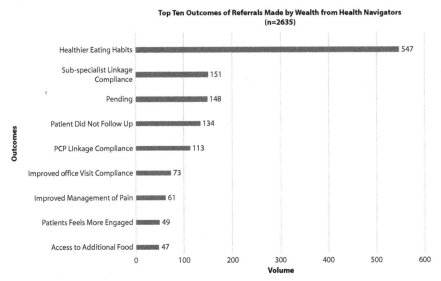

Figure 8: Top Ten Outcomes of Referrals Made by WfH Navigators.

preventive care, and reduces the cost of inappropriate use of emergency rooms and specialists. The navigator can follow up with clinical referrals and be the primary source for community referrals. The top ten referrals and outcomes made for more than 2,600 WfH members enrolled in year two of the program (see Figures 7 and 8) were scheduled during the initial in-personal meetings with navigators.

Other Patient Technology for Communications

Of course, physician responsibility and effectiveness still requires face-to-face dialogue for motivating patients to make earlier and better decisions about their health. In addition to navigation, the Wealth from Health program also promotes valuable technologies to help. Scribes, virtual visits, and the use of other clinical professionals for low acuity care are discussed in details in the chapters that follow. I'm reminded of a "technological advance" demonstrated at a medical conference about a dozen years ago that measured "movement"—of an elderly parent, for example. Well, needless to say, in the trials to demonstrate their efficacy in predicting untoward events, they received a number of complaints from annoyed parents who had received calls from concerned children in other states, protesting their increased resting minutes that day, but that represented nothing more than a harmless exception to their daily schedule.

I found that seeing patients while needing to grapple with an EMR at the same time robbed me of the face time the patient came to expect from me. In fact, when I was stricken with a painful rheumatoid-like issue that affected my joints from a previous parvovirus infection, I eventually found myself sitting across from a leading expert in the field for help. He was absolutely on point with his diagnosis and therapy, but made little eye contact with me because he was totally consumed with putting information into his computer. Not his fault, I might add, but a better way must be found so that this activity does not ultimately lead to complete disenfranchisement with the consumers.

Furthermore, a simple telephone relationship is neither navigational nor particularly effective. Just ask the patients, our consumers. I have a colleague who often states that if the revolution in healthcare is to work, then patients and families have to learn to play by the new rules.

How?

By answering the all-American question: "What's in it for me?"

For the hospital system as the leader in population health, this works in the long run in achieving a healthier population. But the return on investment in the short term helps the CFO provide the dollars for staffing and incentives. Much of the ROI is on decreased readmissions (a CMS reimbursement penalty) through coordination. Also, dollars are tied to decreased use of the ER and inpatient care (ACO metrics) through better understanding of "More care is not better care," our navigator mantra. And the costs are helped by understanding navigators as great communicators who do not need a clinical education. They are often entry-level college graduates who are system oriented and can be mentored quickly on coordination of care throughout the continuum. As mentioned earlier, there are other possible uses for the credits, such as reinforcing the use of high-value care services or eschewing low-value ones.

The Wealth from Health History

In the spirit of these words of wisdom, "In order to see where you going you need to know where you have been," let me briefly recount the history of the Wealth from Health program. The origins extends only back to late 1980s, when an interview I gave to the Associated Press about an incentive-based self-management health program, garnered phone calls from destinations from Australia to Warren, Pennsylvania. In fact, the president of Betts Industries hired us to install the program in his company of 200 employees, spouses, and children. In those days, we used rudimentary materials such as coupon booklets, documentation envelopes, and various stations for the participants to rotate through.

The coupon booklets used by the participants demonstrated evidence as signed off by their providers, attesting to their compliance with their medical regimens. The documentation envelopes helped them gather further evidences of self-management including receipts for bicycle helmets, copies of living wills, even documentation of blood donations. The stations included an exercise box that allowed our team to measure participants' pulses at various intervals, producing an exercise-index level, each level corresponding to a point total. Additionally, one of the stations had a testicular and breast model we used to demonstrate how to examine these areas and what abnormalities felt like. In fact, one year the president informed everyone that if the "Wealth from Health program didn't accomplish anything else it was already worth the investment, because soon after its inception, an employee found a testicular cancer and had already been treated."

In the first year we made three trips to the company, the first orienting everyone to the methodology of the program, the second months later to test them and collect their data, and the last to award their credits earned. The credits were merely the vehicle, as over the years we've used cash, savings bonds, and a host of other rewards, all within CMS guidelines. Health motivating rewards program can also:

- lower out-of-pocket costs for high-value care services;
- inform providers of patient benefits for high-value care services;
- reward people for paying the bill upfront;
- promote healthy utilization of services;
- complete online review or survey;
- reward for showing up for appointments; and
- encourage value-based insurance design with a minimization of the annual rate if requirements are met.

Our WfH reward system (www.wealhfromhealthinc.com and @ WealthhealthNJ on Twitter) has gone through many quality cycles and found a way to keep patients in the system and drive down inappropriate ER visits and inpatient costs (an important metric for the hospital) while increasing quality of life (SF-12 surveys semiannually, an important metric for patients).

The program ran for eight years and was subsequently recreated elsewhere before we unleashed it for patients with chronic disease at JCMC in Jersey City. We have included testimonials from patients. Frankly they are too numerous to recount here. Reference Appendix 1: Selected Achievements by the Wealth from Health Team for some examples. What are we are most proud of? The testimonials as to the "kindness" demonstrated by our people. Priceless.

Care Management Impactability Scores

The pitfall of just targeting the highest risk patients is clear. Some may not be particularly impacted by navigation as much as many in the rising risk category. "Looking within individual risk groups, you see pockets of undiscovered opportunity, or impactability for care management."[180] Prioritizing patients with a score of 200 to 1,000 flags less than 1% of the Medicaid population, but some will lead to a $1,200 to $6,000 average savings per patient receiving care management.

An example where two patients with advanced coronary artery disease, but very different impactability scores:

1. Navigated: Age thirty-nine with two inpatient visits, two ER visits; costs above expected is $0 and an impactability score of 228.
2. Not navigated: Age fifty-three with two inpatient visits and forty-seven ER visits; costs above expected was $2,005 with an impactability score of 1,000.

Bottom line: The same investment in care navigation yields very different results, depending on whom you choose to manage.

Now, stratification of different group members helps us allocate resources, rather than simply dividing equally among the six stratification groups. Please reference the significant change in costs before and after enrollment in the Wealth from Health program, using the patient as their own control and categorized by entry risk category (see Figure 9).

The use of Wealth from Health navigators in the emergency room to direct them ultimately to the metropolitan Federally Qualified Health Center, while also enrolling their participants proved to be quite efficacious.

---

[180] Carlos Jackson, PhD and Annette DuBard, MD, MPH, "Optimizing Targeting for Care Management of Complex Patients," CCNC Data Brief #4 (November 2, 2015). https://www.communitycarenc.org/media/files/data-brief-no-4-optimizing-targeting-cm.pdf.

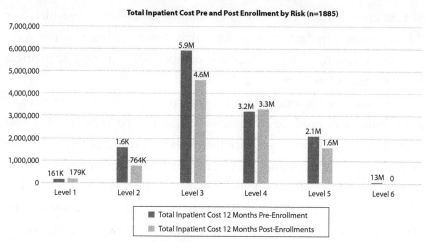

Figure 9: Total Inpatients Cost Pre and Post Enrollment by Risk.

We are firm believers in the KISS (keep it simple, stupid) principle. The videos (available from EmmiSolutions) we show to our patients to educate them on various topics fit the bill perfectly and can be viewed from any device as well as shared with family members. Whereas written materials are by far and away disposed of only most patients, a picture or video is truly worth a thousand words.

The Wealth from Health Pathway to Health

Health systems have done little to focus on patient loyalty or reward programs. In an era of ACOs where patients are free to move between clinicians and healthcare centers, this may prove a costly oversight. Attrition of patients within ACOs is common.[181] Studies have shown that with incentive-based disease control and population-management programs, along with the intervention and assistance of patient navigators, there can be a reduction of healthcare utilization and lead to significant health behavioral changes. However, exaggerating the efficiencies

---

[181]J. Michael McWilliams, MD, PhD, et al., "Outpatient Care Patterns and Organizational Accountability in Medicare," *JAMA* 174 (April 21, 2014).

of care coordination can lead to credibility issues when providers use this argument. In fact, coordination may foster delivery of the right *quantity* of care to each patient, while competition may help keep prices for that care as low as possible.[182]

Establishing ownership over the continuum of care for mergers and acquisitions will produce efficiencies of the new payment models that should allay concerns about price increases for market power. Independent physician groups and ACO programs have performed better, as mentioned previously, when the Wealth from Health program offers incentives for healthy living, self-management of chronic diseases, and adopting patient navigational services. The WfH reward points system was created to provide the patient navigator an innovative pathway for education and service allocation and to allow the patients and their caregivers to learn how to navigate through the healthcare system and be incentivized by doing so.

Wealth from Health Successes

The Wealth from Health program has helped more than 4,000 patients learn how to better manage their chronic disease(s) over the past twenty years. In addition, patient navigators supported patient engagement, education, and empowerment in many different settings, as discussed elsewhere in this book. The program reduced admissions and ER visits at a cost savings of more than $5 million. To date this extremely innovative concept has been awarded the Hearst finalist, Gage, and New Jersey Health Hero awards.

Health systems have done little to focus on patient loyalty or reward programs in an era of ACOs where patients are free to move between clinicians and healthcare centers. To illustrate the comprehensive nature

---

[182] J. Michael McWilliams, MD, PhD, "Cost Containment and the Tale of Care Coordination," *NEJM* 375 (December 8, 2016).

of the program and just how valuable Wealth from Health navigators are to our patients with chronic disease(s) the following represents the wide swath of questions and issues that they deal with:

Orienting to the Healthcare System

* Who do I need to see for care now?
* Where do I go for care?
* What type of doctors will I be seeing in the system?
* Can I stay in my community for care?
* Who is the expert in this field?
* What are the contact numbers for my healthcare team?
* Who do I call evenings and on weekends?
* Can I ask my questions to the healthcare team electronically?

Utilizing Community Resources

* Is there free legal aid available?
* Are there agencies to help with medications? Can I get financial help in my community?
* Are there people\groups that can help with transportation?
* Can someone clean my house?
* Are there other patients I can talk with?

Providing Emotional Support for Patients

* I cannot grasp all that is happening to me; who can I talk with?
* I do not feel comfortable in groups. Is there someone I can talk with?
* Will I be able to work?

- Is there someone to discuss financial concerns?
- What do I tell my children?
- Who can talk to my spouse\partner?

Assisting Patients with Logistics, Such as Transportation and Costs

- Is there transportation assistance?
- I live far away. Is there an affordable place to stay?
- Directions for the appointment\test?
- Is there an interpreter available for me\my family?
- Who could help me with the copays?
- I am overwhelmed with the insurance forms; who could help me?
- Who do I see about my short-term and long-term disability?
- Is there childcare available?
- Can someone help me with my Living Will? Can you help?

Advocating for the Patient

- I am frustrated with by the billing, because another one came from the same visit. Are they all bills?
- Can you review my care plan with me?
- I did not feel comfortable asking questions; what did the doctor mean?
- I feel dissatisfied with my care; can you help me?

Providing Education on a Diagnosis, (for example, of cancer)

1. What type of cancer do I have? Are there different types of my cancers?

2. What are good Internet resources?

3. What tests\scans will be performed?

4. What is the treatment for my cancer?

5. What can I expect after surgery?

6. What can I expect after my first chemotherapy treatment?

7. What is radiation like?

8. What can I expect at the surgeons\medical oncologist\radiation visit?

9. What is a survivorship care plan?

10. What did the doctor mean by palliative care?

Examples of Wealth from Health Navigational Accomplishments

Commercial payers like Horizon BC/BS who did not wish to fall too far behind the government in demonstrating their progressive agenda, decided to add care coordination dollars on a PM/PM (per member per month) basis, but failed to substantially alter the healthcare landscape previously described. They and many insurers, indeed healthcare systems, pay lip service to navigation or care coordination, by maintaining telephone bank nurses who call periodically. There needs to be a connection with at a minimum, one face-to-face meeting, to truly bear the fruits of this activity.

Wealth from Health navigation has demonstrated just this. I am reminded of how the for profit companies that participated in the Disease Management Association of America arranged for Medicare to conduct a large-scale randomized clinical trial of hundreds of thousand patients being managed using just telephone support with the control arm of a sizable number not getting any telephone support. The study was stopped early because their activities proved to be more costly and not very effective. These are activities should be proof that what is needed between providers and patients is a relationship that is mature and honest.

Behavioral economics and human behavior have helped shape the Wealth from Health program. It is not just the size of the incentive but also its design and delivery. The same sized incentive could affect behavior differently, depending on whether it is framed as a gain or loss, presented to people privately or in front of a group, perceived as fair or unfair, and so forth.[183] In one large Wealth from Health group, dollars were awarded, and another savings bonds, and another gift certificates, the possibilities go on and on. There has definitely been a paradigm shift. "The most successful hospitals that listen to what customers want and give it to them. It is that simple."[184]

The following describe just a few typical specific WfH navigational wins:

- Conducted risk assessment and identified that a patient's recent admissions were due to back/leg pain. Patient further explained that she was no longer receiving physical therapy, and as result her pain has resumed. Navigator obtained referral from patient's primary care physician for physical therapy services and referred patient to JCMC outpatient physical therapy. Patient is currently receiving therapy three times a week and has reported feeling better. Patient has not been admitted to JCMC since starting therapy.
- Received a phone call from a current member, asking if navigator could assist her son who was suffering from high blood pressure; however son was homeless and not linked to any services. Navigator met with patient's son and enrolled him in the program. Navigator conducted assessment, identified several barriers with patient, and created a checklist of issues to address. Due to patient having no form of identification to apply for Medicaid or to go to a

---

[183] D. Khullar, MPP, et al., "Behavioral Economics and Physician Compensation-Promise and Challenge," *NEJM* 372 (June 11, 2015).

[184] Quint Studer, *Hardwiring Excellence* (Gulf Breeze, FL: Fire Starter Publishing, 2003), 2–44.

federally qualified health center (FQHC), the navigator linked him to medical records at JCMC, which enabled him to obtain necessary paperwork to reapply for social security card. Navigator also provided the patient with a WfH member ID card that included his date of birth, which allowed him to have proof of identity. Next navigator linked the patient to an FQHC for medical treatment, and patient applied for Medicaid.

- A patient's chronic seizures landed her in the ER at JCMC on a weekly basis. She'd see a doctor, be handed some medication, and sent on her way. A Wealth from Health navigator was able to set up a consult with an epilepsy specialist. When the doctor told her she needed more vitamin D and should eat more dairy, the navigator gave her a list of foods she could buy at the supermarket and assisted her in obtaining medication from a state program. As of today, patient is an active member of the WfH program and hasn't had a seizure.

- Patient joined our Wealth from Health program 2013. One his biggest issues was understanding his insurance carrier; he wasn't sure where his benefit card was accepted for outpatient services. His only request was to have access to a wound care center he could visit on a weekly basis. Navigator was able to find him a wound care center ten minutes away from his home, as well as free transportation for every booked appointment the entire month.

- Patient had a colon procedure in 2014. She currently receives intravenous magnesium infusions due to electrolyte abnormalities after colon resection. Her main concern was getting back and forth to the hospital to receive more IV fluid due to constant dehydration. Her WfH navigator was able to connect her with Home Solutions Infusion Therapy Center. The company now visits her every day at her home to provide IV infusion. Patient even became capable of doing the infusions herself, so Home Solutions has the option to drop off all the materials.

GOOD-BYE TO FEE FOR SERVICE: A MUST

The fee-for-service (FFS) payment model aspect of the American healthcare system, by far, represents the most important cause of high healthcare expenditures in the United States. How? By incentivizing more tests, more services, duplication, and ignoring care coordination and efficiencies. Other reasons for the current healthcare morass discussed in this book prevail, but there can be no course correction, revamping, or hope for a better system if this disincentive for change is allowed to stand. Steven A. Schroeder, MD and William Frist, MD, representing the National Commission on Physician Payment Reform, wrote a compelling article in the *New England Journal of Medicine*,[185] detailing how we can phase out fee for service over time, which we have summarized:

- Payers must eliminate FFS to medical practices.
- Transition to a new model(s) of care over five years based on quality and value. (see below)

---

[185] Steven Schroeder, MD, et al., "Phasing Out Fee-for-Service Payment," *NEJM* 368.21 (May 23, 2013).

- While FFS continues during this period, recalibrate to include quality metrics and substantial reward for achieving them.
- Value evaluation and management codes.
- Payment to favor locations where costs are less veer from "edifice complex" thinking.
- Equal payments to providers, despite subspecialty designations, for equal services.
- Encourage smaller practices to collaborate virtually with similar practices to save on expenses.
- Start with the sickest 5% of patients in this new system.
- Ensure access to high quality care.
- Medicare needs to concentrate on eliminating inappropriate utilization of services and ensure that its relative value units are accurate and continuously updated.

Failure to align compensation incentives with reform goals now may increase the risk of penalties for overutilization of acute care or diagnostic services by the old volume-based practice mind-set. This mentality takes some time to imprint and cannot be turned on with a snap of the fingers. The kinds of intentions described here cannot address problematic choices that are influenced by economics, such overuse or underuse of erythropoiesis-stimulating agents by dialysis centers because of payment incentives or questionable zone chemotherapy choices, which can drive the revenue of oncologists and institutions that depend on such treatments for their economic success. Upton Sinclair wrote, "It is difficult for a man to understand something when his salary depends on not understanding it."[186]

---

[186] Jerry Avorn, MD, "The Psychology of Clinical Decision Making—Implications for Medication Use," *NEJM* 378. 8 (February 22, 2018).

The BDC Advisor Group favors this approach:[187]

1. Create a Physician Compensation Committee that should begin with education sessions on physician compensation market data, regulatory issues related to achieving fair market value, and the options in physician compensation models.
2. Move to a flexible compensation plan that uses a blend of three or more national physician compensation surveys to determine the current market. It will need to be able to evolve over time.
3. Build your primary compensation plan first. The compensation model for primary care physicians should promote "teaming" and outcomes not independence and volume. To do so, the need to pro-actively work with the patient and specialists to coordinate care.
4. Offer a guaranteed salary based on years of experience.
5. Create incentives for access, clinical quality, service quality, efficiency, productivity and citizenship.
6. Institute a panel management fee.
7. Take advantage of important metrics: reward patient access to high-quality care at the lowest reasonable cost and of highest importance to patients.
8. Maintain continuous communication and an open feedback loop: hospital CEOs need to explain exactly why they are doing what they are doing.
9. Consistently move to more performance-based compensation: When the group moves to a 25–30% value-based reimbursement figure and then a greater than 50% figure, where the majority of revenue is from value-based contracts, the physicians should be well versed in the strategy of goals of the health system at that point.

---

[187] Phyllis Floyd, MD, "Roadmap for Physician Compensation in a Value-Based World," BDC Advisors, September/October 2014. http://www.bdcadvisors.com/roadmap-for-physician-compensation-in-a-value-based-world/.

In situations where Medicaid represents one of the biggest insurers, specifically in academic medical centers, a more strategic outlook similar to the one we present in total here, particularly resonates as the Medicaid expansion initiated with the ACA will essentially remain intact.[188] Medicaid consists of four enrollment groups:

1. Elderly (covers long-term care);
2. Disabled, which includes people with multiple chronic comorbidities and often accompanying behavioral-health issues;
3. Healthy adults who are poor (main target of the expansion); and
4. Children.

The expansion is uneven around the country and differences exist across the states in this way:

- Whether federal expansion funds were accepted from ACA.
- State payment rates and overall spending per adult enrollee.
- Size of the expansion relative to overall state Medicaid program.
- State's Medicaid Managed Care policies.

State policymakers are keen to be innovative now more than ever though new creative delivery systems must be established. Only then can the following value-based structure make sense:

- Global risk for a population;
- Integrated primary care acute and chronic bundles; and
- Total care for special-needs populations.

---

[188] Michael Schwartz, MBA, MS, et al., "Creating Value in the Medicaid Expansion: A Strategic Framework for AMCs," BDC Advisors, October 2107. http://www.bdcadvisors.com/creating-value-medicaid-expansion-strategic-framework-amcs/.

"Believe it or not, most organizations do not look at the populations in a systematic, quantitatively rigorous way and figure out what services are needed and how that matches up with what they're good at and not good at or how they're networks are designed," says Francois de Brantes, vice president and director of the Health Care Incentives Improvement Institute at the Altarum Institute, a not-for-profit organization.

- Phasing out fee for service (FFS)—necessary actions.
- Payers must eliminate FFS to medical practices.
- Transition to a new model(s) of care over five years based on quality and value.
- While FFS continues during this period, recalibrate to include quality metrics and substantial reward for achieving them.
- Value evaluation and management codes.
- Payment to favor locations where costs are less, veer from "edifice complex" thinking.
- Equal payments to providers, despite subspecialty designations, for equal services.
- Encourage smaller practices to collaborate virtually with similar practices to save on expenses.
- Start with the sickest 5% of patients in this new system.
- Ensure access to high-quality care.
- Medicare needs to concentrate on eliminating inappropriate utilization of services and ensure that its relative value units are accurate and continuously updated.

HOW IT ALL BEGAN

I t happened innocently enough. A typical Sunday night at the Ratner household. Having just finished dinner and the necessary cleanup (my job always as I cannot, or will not, cook) I got comfortable as *Sixty Minutes* began.

"Doug, a resident is on the phone. Needs to speak with you right away," my wife called into the living room.

"Ugh, okay," I grunted as I reluctantly gave up my perch on the couch.

"Dr. Ratner, it's Alfonso; sorry to bother you, sir." Alfonso was one of my best residents and the most dependable as I trusted him more than other residents to be my eyes and ears if I couldn't be onsite when on-call. "Sir, we have a bona fide Goodpasture's syndrome admitted tonight to your service. He came with a stack of papers detailing his entire history. He's a thirty-two-year-old Air Force pilot just recently back from the Gulf War. Biopsy proven, positive anti-glomerular basement membrane antibody, Ommaya reservoir in his left supraclavicular region, urine loaded with red blood cells."

I loved this guy: no nonsense and to the point. The staccato delivery gave me all the pertinent facts. This patient had a proven rare disease that had required an indwelling catheter to help with medication delivery.

"How is he doing clinically?" I asked.

"Severe pain, otherwise stable."

Renal colic given red cells (blood) in the urine and pain? I had never taken care of a patient with this condition before, but these patients do bleed in their kidneys and sometimes lungs. An internist, even one involved in a teaching program all of his professional life, may see only one case in a career. To date, I have seen two.

"He's getting a morphine IV to make him comfortable," Alfonso continued.

Sounded plausible. I said, "Make sure you start high-dose steroids. Have rheumatology see him, and we need to alert the plasmapheresis team to cleanse his blood of the abnormal proteins." I paused to think of other issues. "What's his creatinine (kidney), pulse oximetry (lung)?"

"Both good at 1.2 and 98% on room air," Alfonso responded immediately.

Alfonso is good, anticipates all question appropriately. "Call me if anything changes, I will see him in the morning unless of course you need me to come in now."

"Not necessary, sir."

Needless to say, the next four days could only be described as something straight out of a *Disorder* (not *Murder*) *on the Orient Express* movie. Monday morning, I rounded early and made a beeline to this enigmatic patient's room first though I had also received five additional admissions in total from Sunday night. Here is what I witnessed: A nice looking, well-built, thirty-two-year-old African-American male sitting up comfortably in bed discussing his imminent awarding of the Medal of Honor for his heroism in the Gulf War, helping to push the Iraqis back behind the Kuwait border. Unbeknown to me, my resident had already purchased a phone connection for our patient who requested it so, "President Bush would be able to call me directly," as he clearly wouldn't be able to travel to Washington, D.C. himself. The call would have to suffice.

While sitting on the edge of the bed after having examined him (his physical exam was totally normal), I reviewed the thirty-page record he had produced on admission, holes neatly punched so as to facilitate it is inclusion in the medical record, including his entire workup and treatment regimens over the past few years. Keep reading there is a point to this story.

My team's next order of business was to collect some urine, take it to the lab, place in the centrifuge for five minutes, pour off the top layer, and analyze the remaining "sediment" under the microscope. That is precisely what we did, looking for red blood cells casts (clumps) of misshapen red blood cells characteristic of this highly unusual malady. We saw neither—just urine chock full of normal red blood cells, as if someone had poured a few drops of blood into the urine sample itself. I suppose you realize by now that our man was the Great Impostor, but I am getting ahead of myself.

All efforts to confirm his medical history by way of the Armed Services were fruitless. All attempts to reach family members, equally futile. Meanwhile, on day two he spiked a high fever of 105°F, though he looked comfortable all the while. Patients with fevers this high, invariably, look and act sick. The break in the case? The nurses who took care of him on a moment-to-moment basis.

"There is something really fishy about this guy," they commented to me on two separate occasions. Always listen to members of your team: one for all physicians. We became convinced his medical history story was false.

As luck would have it, that week's *New England Journal of Medicine* (*NEJM* is the gold standard of medical literature) contained a case entitled "The Red Baron."[189] It described our guy, who had stolen paperwork from a fellow serviceman, had thirteen admissions on the East Coast in one year's time period, underwent three separate renal

---

[189] T.P. Duffy, "The Red Baron," *NEJM* 327 (Aug 6, 1992).

(kidney) biopsies, and had an Ommaya reservoir placed near his shoulder to receive powerful medications. Furthermore, he was accessing this reservoir for blood (placed under the skin and into a blood vessel) via his own syringes (most likely stolen) and injecting them into his urine to perpetrate the hoax.

Why? To receive attention and receive powerful narcotics for his "renal colic." We confronted him with the article, which elicited an irate response from him, questioning our integrity and intelligence for connecting him to the patient in the article. He subsequently signed out AMA (against medical advice). Months later he surfaced in a hospital in the Hell's Kitchen area of Manhattan, this time suffering from tuberculosis, undoubtedly due to the long-term consequences of the steroids and other immunosuppressive drugs he had received under the pretense of having someone else's disease.

Why did I choose to recount this story to begin this book?

I am highlighting how monumental a journey we have embarked upon by detailing my thoughts during that most interesting week early in my medical career. I remember commenting to a colleague, "Our job is difficult enough without a Munchausen (patient who fakes disease) going to such great lengths to fool not only me, but at least a dozen different physicians over the course of one year."

Worse yet, I am certain we were not the only ones to question the veracity of this patient, hence the *NEJM* article. The financial and physically harming costs for treating him were tied to the wrong diagnosis and the "telephone tag" that happens all too often today, just one of the problems we face in righting this healthcare ship that is badly listing. Lastly, a number of nephrologists candidly admitted in the article that they retrofitted their microscopic exam to correspond with the purported diagnosis. A vivid example of how "the mind sees what it wants to see," despite evidence to the contrary, a subject covered in the chapter on diagnostic excellence.

Though this example and some of the preceding chapters may appear to take harsh aim at the healthcare field and professionals, our comprehensive assault and aggressive, thoughtful solutions to right this ship are also included. The issues are fixable, we believe, but please read thoughtfully and make up your own minds. If you conclude the same, then it is incumbent on you to participate in the solutions, either recreating ours or developing your own.

Finally, let me wax philosophically for a moment. Turning the ripe old age of sixty-five, I find myself contemplating issues like, "What really constitutes a life well lived?" Loving and being loved back, certainly. But if we were to fast-forward our lives to one week before we leave this Earth, what would we wish for? More money to leave our children? Maybe. Leaving this world a little bit better? Maybe. But one thing is certain: All humans take actions directed at making ourselves happy, secure, less anxious, and so forth. The result is a world where self-interest often guides what we all do.

The world of medicine is no exception, although it wasn't conceived that way. What is my point? What if a world existed where we allowed ourselves to challenge and subvert these instincts and instead work for the greater good as it relates to this marvelous field? Only then can the stage be set for a monumental renaissance in health. As physicians, we start our careers to do "good," and often end it with a goal to do financially "well." Can't we finish with good while knowing we will do well enough? Today, this difference has never been more important.

Douglas Ratner, MD 2021

JERSEY CITY MEDICAL CENTER-RWJ BARNABAS HEALTH SYSTEM'S QUALITY IMPROVEMENT PROJECTS INITIATIVE— AN ABBREVIATED LIST OF MEDICAL STUDENT PROJECTS

1. <u>Reducing Readmissions for Chronic Heart Failure.</u> Rohan Dame, Alexa Gavaga, Davey Ho-Sang, Ethan Isidro, and Louis Alerte, MS. Poster presentation: Jersey City Medical Center, RWJ Barnabas Health System's Quality Improvement Projects Initiative. January 2016, Jersey City, N.J.
   Goals:
   - Decrease number of thirty-day readmissions for patients with CHF.
   - Streamline and simplify the follow-up pathway for recently discharged CHF patients.
   - Improve the transition of care between organizations in order to decrease overlap in responsibilities in the post-discharge setting.
   - Improve monitoring and documentation of patient activity/ condition in the thirty-day post-discharge window.

2. <u>Assessing Transportation Barriers in CHF Patients</u>. Miguel De Leon, Mohammad Baddad, Louis Alerte. Poster presentation: Jersey City Medical Center, RWJ Barnabas Health System's Quality Improvement Projects Initiative. February 2016, Jersey City, N.J. Goals:
   - Create a stratification tool that more accurately reflects a patient's barrier to transportation, thus properly assessing patient transportation needs.
   - Provide patients who are at greatest risk for transportation barriers with transportation resources.

3. <u>Patient Care Beyond Hospital Walls: A Slightly Different Case Presentation</u>. Jason Cummings and Louis Alerte. Oral presentation: Jersey City Medical Center—RWJ Barnabas Health System's Quality Improvement Projects Initiative. February 2016, Jersey City, N.J. Goals:
   - Improving the way history and physicals are assessed.
   - Improving the continuum of care.

4. <u>The Need to Address Obesity and Type II DM in Pediatrics</u>. Divya Kanneganti and Louis Alerte. Poster presentation: Jersey City Medical Center, RWJ Barnabas Health System's Quality Improvement Projects Initiative. July 2016, Jersey City, N.J. Goals:
   - To expand the services offered by the Wealth from Health program to create a wellness program for pediatrics.
   - To reduce pediatric visits due to obesity and DM II by 25% within five years.

5. <u>Reduce Visits Due to Sickle Cell Disease by Improved Care Coordination</u>. Trent Worrell, Jennyfer Morel, and Louis Alerte. Poster presentation: Jersey City Medical Center, RWJ Barnabas Health System's Quality Improvement Projects Initiative. July 2016, Jersey City, N.J.

Goals:
- To reduce ER and inpatient utilization rates.
- To improve care coordination and patient engagement upon discharge from the hospital.
- Increase sickle cell awareness within the organization and the community.
- To establish partnerships in the community to improve SCD management.

6. Right-sizing the Use of Radiographic Imaging. Edidiong Inyang and Louis Alerte. Poster presentation: Jersey City Medical Center, RWJ Barnabas Health System's Quality Improvement Projects Initiative. August 2016, Jersey City, N.J.

   Goal: eliminate unnecessary use of said imaging with the use of appropriate guidelines.

7. Using Evidence Based Practice to Prevent Overuse of Common Serum Rheumatologic Tests. Janish Kothari, Edidiong Inyang, and Louis Alerte. Poster presentation: Jersey City Medical Center, RWJ Barnabas Health System's Quality Improvement Projects Initiative. August 2016, Jersey City, N.J.

   Goal: reduce by 15% the number of rheumatologic markers per annum.

8. Reducing Cesarean Deliveries in Nulliparous Women. Rachel Bernstein and Louis Alerte. Poster presentation: Jersey City Medical Center, RWJ Barnabas Health System's Quality Improvement Projects Initiative. September 2016, Jersey City, N.J.

   Goal: reduce the overall cesarean section rate to 24% with significant reduction of NSVT cesarean deliveries.

9. Managing Obesity and Diabetes for Patients with Behavioral Health Conditions. Kunal Mehta and Louis Alerte. Poster presentation: Jersey City Medical Center, RWJ Barnabas Health System's Quality Improvement Projects Initiative. September 2016, Jersey City, NJ.

Goal: align treatment plans to reduce the effects of depression on the morbidity of patients with obesity and diabetes.

10. Diversity & Inclusion: LGBTQ in Healthcare. Melanie Graber, Alisha Ghosh, and Louis Alerte. Poster presentation: Jersey City Medical Center, RWJ Barnabas Health System's Quality Improvement Projects Initiative. September 2016, Jersey City, N.J.

    Goal: obtain concrete information on our LGBTQ population with the ultimate goal of implementing strategies at JCMC and associated clinics which address their identified needs.

11. Increase POLST / Advance Directives While Reducing EoLC Cost. Dhruvin Mehta, Rahul Yadav, and Louis Alerte. Poster presentation: Jersey City Medical Center, RWJ Barnabas Health System's Quality Improvement Projects Initiative. September 2016, Jersey City, N.J.

    Goal: eliminate unnecessary treatments associated with high mortality and reduce EoLC with the use of appropriate guidelines.

12. Symptoms Relief Management. Dhruvin Mehta, Rahul Yadav, Melanie Graber, Kunal Mehta, Rachel Bernstein, and Louis Alerte. Poster presentation: Jersey City Medical Center, RWJ Barnabas Health System's Quality Improvement Projects Initiative. September 2016, Jersey City, N.J.

SELECTED ACHIEVEMENTS BY THE WEALTH FROM HEALTH TEAM

1. Created the Wealth from Health program and credit-system methodology that taught self-management of chronic disease (over 4,000 patients in three separate venues), resulting in well over $5 million dollars in savings over twenty years by significantly reducing admissions, readmissions, and observation stays; program has been copied by other organizations.
2. Appointed by the N.J. governor to chair *The Disease Management Study Commission*, which I conceived and collaborated with N.J. politicians.
3. Drove cost savings of $144,712 in 2015 and $120,582 through an *Antimicrobial Stewardship Program* when medication or delivery is incorrect.
4. Decreased LOS in medical ICU from 10.3 days in 2015 to 8.5 days in 2016 with a *Mobility and Sedation program* dedicated in ICU.
5. Piloted *Help the Helpers* to address caregiver needs with all participants remaining through 2016.
6. Promoted a *Wealth from Health Oncology navigational program* (100 members) and a Cancer prehabilitation program entitled, *Getting Stronger*.

7. Initiated *Community Health Trust* collaboration between eighty local businesses and services at discounted rate for patients where social circumstance impedes health, serving over 3,000 members so far.

8. Implemented *new sickle cell* protocols, resulting in LOS decrease to 3.43 days from over 4.25 days in 2016.

9. *"Clot-Busting"* program education on enoxaparin injection technique, potentially saving $33,000 through LOS decrease.

10. Initiated the *Teleneurology Program* that led to a 38% reduction in door to needle TPA administration the first year.

11. Created *a Hepatology Center* that screened 3,689 patients the first year, with fifty patients successfully undergoing Hep C treatment.

12. Began a *Transfusion Stewardship Program* that led to an 11% reduction in RBC transfusions and began a TEG program to right-size coagulation replacement products during bleeding episodes.

13. Started a *postacute care initiative with SNFists* in the SNFs with a 32% reduction in LOS the first year.

14. Advocated and oversaw the first *Bundle Payment Initiative at JCMC (BPCI)* with overall physician payments for 2014–2016 amounting to $271,495 and JCMC revenue of $1,466,891 for same period.

15. *Pediatric Asthma DSRIP Initiative* that delivered complex case management for 1,408 patients, including an Environmental House-call™ audit of each child's home, fifty-seven in total.

16. Created the *first JCMC Observation Unit* that averaged between 3,500–5,000 patients /year over its five year course, resulting in an average LOS of twenty hours in 2017.

17. Created the *Race to Zero Program*™ to emphasize symptom reduction as a hallmark for palliative care with an improvement from 42% to 72% in 2017 symptom reduction and a 37.5% withdrawal of life prolonging interventions, up from 25%.

18. Created a *Renal-Rheumatology Clinic* that conjointly followed twenty-three SLE patients; data not yet in.

ABOUT THE AUTHORS

Douglas Ratner, MD is the retired Chair of Medicine at Jersey City Medical Center-RWJ Barnabas Health (JCMC), the largest health system in New Jersey. In that role he was instrumental in the sea change that transformed the hospital from an urban trauma hospital dependent on state funding to meet payroll to one with a robust bottom line. He most recently chaired the N.J. Commission on Chronic Disease Management, which created a public document as a roadmap to better health regardless of insurance status. In 1996 he created Wealth from Health, Inc. as a stand-alone patient rewards program and first successfully implemented it at a Pennsylvania corporation.

At JCMC, Wealth from Health, Inc. has grown to encompass all aspects of population health initiatives. Dr. Ratner is author of the seminal work, *Tomorrow's Health for Today's Family. A Groundbreaking Guide to Better Health for You and Your Community in the 21st Century.* His Wealth from Health programs have been nationally recognized for innovation by both the American Essential Hospitals Association and the Hearst Foundation.

Susan Walsh, MD, FACP is recently retired from the positions of Vice President of Population Health, ACO Medical Director, and Program Director for the RWJBH-JCMC internal medicine residency. Prior to her position at JCMC, she was Deputy Commissioner of Health for the state of New Jersey and charged with all issues pertaining to public health, including equity and access, epidemiology, the creation of the N.J. medical marijuana program and the state's laboratory, and state-wide response teams. Her skills in forging partnerships led to the formation of the Greater Newark Health Care Coalition and the Trenton Health Plan, which continue to bring CEOs and community advocates together to find solutions for barriers to care. As VP of Clinical Affairs and Chief Medical Officer, she also has an extensive background in managing federally qualified health centers that seek to provide superior care to the critically underserved populations.

CPSIA information can be obtained
at www.ICGtesting.com
Printed in the USA
BVHW040348100421
604642BV00003B/12